Residential Green
Valuation Tools

by Sandra K. Adomatis, SRA, LEED Green Associate

Appraisal Institute • 200 W. Madison • Suite 1500 • Chicago, IL 60606 • www.appraisalinstitute.org

The Appraisal Institute advances global standards, methodologies, and practices through the professional development of property economics worldwide.

Reviewers: Stephanie Coleman, MAI, SRA
Thomas A. Dorsey, MAI, SRA, LEED AP
Kevin Morrow, NAHB
Laura Reedy Stukel, NAR Green, EcoBroker Certified

Chief Executive Officer: Frederick H. Grubbe
Director of Communications: Ken Chitester
Senior Manager, Publications: Stephanie Shea-Joyce
Senior Book Editor/Technical Writer: Michael McKinley
Senior Technical Book Editor: Emily Ruzich
Manager, Book Design/Production: Michael Landis

For Educational Purposes Only

The materials presented in this text represent the opinions and views of the author. Although these materials may have been reviewed by members of the Appraisal Institute, the views and opinions expressed herein are not endorsed or approved by the Appraisal Institute as policy unless adopted by the Board of Directors pursuant to the Bylaws of the Appraisal Institute. While substantial care has been taken to provide accurate and current data and information, the Appraisal Institute does not warrant the accuracy or timeliness of the data and information contained herein. Further, any principles and conclusions presented in this publication are subject to court decisions and to local, state and federal laws and regulations and any revisions of such laws and regulations.

This book is sold for educational and informational purposes only with the understanding that the Appraisal Institute is not engaged in rendering legal, accounting or other professional advice or services. Nothing in these materials is to be construed as the offering of such advice or services. If expert advice or services are required, readers are responsible for obtaining such advice or services from appropriate professionals.

Nondiscrimination Policy

The Appraisal Institute advocates equal opportunity and nondiscrimination in the appraisal profession and conducts its activities in accordance with applicable federal, state, and local laws.

Library of Congress Cataloging-in-Publication Data

Adomatis, Sandra K., 1952-
 Residential green valuation tools / by Sandra K. Adomatis, SRA, LEED Green Associate.
   pages cm
 Includes bibliographical references.
 ISBN 978-1-935328-52-0
 1. Real property--Valuation. 2. Ecological houses--Valuation. 3. Sustainable buildings. I. Title.
   HD1387.A36 2014
   333.33'82--dc23

                                                                              2014002724

Table of Contents

About the Author

Sandra K. Adomatis, SRA, LEED Green Associate, is a practicing real property appraiser and consultant at Adomatis Appraisal Service in Punta Gorda, Florida, where she is involved in a variety of residential and small commercial property appraisals. She is a state-certified general appraiser and has been an active member of the Appraisal Institute since 1985. She earned her LEED Green Associate credential from the Green Building Certification Institute in 2013.

Sandra is a current member of the Appraisal Institute's Admissions and Designation Qualifications Committee and past vice chair of the national Education Committee. In 2009, she served as the Appraisal Institute's West Coast Florida Chapter President. *The Appraisal Journal* has published three of her articles about high-performance properties. Sandra has edited and contributed to Appraisal Institute books, courses, and seminars, including the Valuation of Sustainable Buildings professional development program. For more than 15 years, she has been involved in instructing seminars and courses for the Appraisal Institute. She was presented with the Appraisal Institute's President's Award by Richard L. Borges II, MAI, SRA, in 2013, and in 2012 she received the Dr. William N. Kinnard, Jr. Award from the Appraisal Institute Education Trust.

Over the last few years, Sandra has become the voice of "green" from the Appraisal Institute, both within and outside the organization. She has spoken to thousands of appraisers, Realtors, builders, and others in the real estate industry at national events hosted by groups such as the National Association of Home Builders, the National Association of Realtors, the Best Practices Research Alliance, and the Alliance for Environmental Sustainability.

Sandra resides in Punta Gorda, Florida, with her husband and mentor, Richard Adomatis, MAI.

Acknowledgments

SITE WATER ENERGY AIR QUALITY MATERIALS MAINTENANCE

Several reviewers provided valuable content and suggestions, including Laura Reedy Stukel, NAR Green, EcoBroker Certified, Kevin Morrow of the National Association of Home Builders, and Thomas A. Dorsey, MAI, SRA, LEED AP. The success of this book was not possible without the efforts of those named and unnamed, along with numerous individuals who provided resources, research, graphics, case studies, and the encouragement to persevere. Special thanks go to Appraisal Institute Immediate Past President Richard L. Borges II, MAI, SRA, for his encouragement and numerous articles on high-performance topics.

I would also like to express my gratitude to Stephanie Shea-Joyce, Senior Manager of Publications at the Appraisal Institute, who was relentless in her appeal to write a book on green valuation. Because of her encouragement and the excellent staff of editors, this book was born. What I did not expect is that I would have two editors, Emily Ruzich and Michael McKinley, who both have a passion for green topics. Words cannot express the gratitude I have for Michael and Emily's part in making this book a reality through hours of guidance, constructive critique, and wordsmithery.

I would like to express my heartfelt thanks to my husband, Richard Adomatis, MAI, for his inspiration, patience during my year of writing, and years of mentoring me into the appraiser I am today.

Sandra K. Adomatis, SRA, LEED Green Associate

Foreword

SITE WATER ENERGY AIR QUALITY MATERIALS MAINTENANCE

The market for green, or high-performance, homes is clearly grow-ing, and appraisers who want to appraise these homes competently need to stay up-to-date on the latest green terms, home features, and organizations. *Residential Green Valuation Tools* explains what the term *green* means as it applies to housing and how to determine ex-actly how green a particular property is.

In this book, author Sandra K. Adomatis, SRA, provides a com-prehensive overview of green housing and the valuation of high-performance homes. The main elements of green homes—site, water and energy efficiency, indoor air quality, materials, and operations and maintenance—are explained, and case studies are presented to illustrate common scenarios and challenges that arise when valuing high-performance homes. In-depth guidance is provided on properly completing the Appraisal Institute's Residential Green and Energy Ef-ficient Addendum form for appraisal reports. The valuation of Energy Star homes, passive solar houses, solar photovoltaic systems, and net-zero energy homes is also discussed.

Appraising green homes presents some complications and chal-lenges, and *Residential Green Valuation Tools* explains the methods and resources you need to become a green-friendly appraiser.

Ken P. Wilson, MAI, SRA
2014 President
Appraisal Institute

Defining *Green* and Understanding the Elements of Green Building

Money, furniture, cleaning products, and buildings are just a few of the things that may be classified as "green." But if the green label can apply to so many different things, is your definition of the term likely to be the same as your neighbor's? When applied to houses, *green* takes on a variety of meanings, and this creates difficulty in the marketplace. Even the different organizations that certify buildings as green for the benefit of property owners and other market participants use a variety of definitions for the term. However, all of these definitions usually point toward the same six elements of green building:

- Site
- Water efficiency
- Energy efficiency
- Indoor air quality
- Materials
- Operations and maintenance

If everyone's definition of *green building* included these six elements of green building, we would have less confusion and most likely an increased market acceptance of the concept.

The following definition of *green building* from the US Environmental Protection Agency (www.epa.gov/greenbuildings/pubs/about.htm) will be used for the purposes of this book:

> **green building.** The practice of creating structures and using processes that are environmentally responsible and resource-efficient throughout a building's life-cycle from siting to design, construction, operation, maintenance, renovation, and deconstruction. This practice expands and complements the classical building design concerns of economy, utility, durability, and comfort. Green building is also known as sustainable or high-performance building.

After eight years of studying green building and dealing with client's numerous interpretations of that term, I have come to the conclusion that *high-performance* is a better term to use to describe green building technology. The use of the term *high-performance* does not allow for as much misunderstanding as the use of the term *green*. A house described as *high-performance* would obviously perform at a higher level than a house built to traditional minimum specifications and capacities, whereas a house described as *green* would be subject to broad interpretation and misinterpretation.

It is safe to say that all homeowners want their buildings to perform better. Consider the commercial tagline I once saw on a sign for a residential development in Salt Lake City: "Here, *home* is a verb." This says it all: a home should work for you instead of you relentlessly working for it. Keeping this tagline in mind as we work through the valuation and market issues of green building will make it easier to grasp the concepts of performance in relation to value.

This sign in front of a site marked for residential development in Salt Lake City presents an important concept: A home should work for its owner, rather than the owner working relentlessly for the home.

However, before premiums for performance can be established and paid, the market must be convinced that the high-performance features have value, which is not the responsibility of appraisers. Builders, agents, certifying organizations, and government entities promoting high-performance building have that responsibility. Appraisers are charged with understanding the building technology and measuring the market's reaction to its value.

I once had a conversation with a pair of homeowners that illustrates what you might hear when discussing green building with someone outside the industry. When I first brought up the topic of green building in the conversation, the woman quickly stated that she did not "believe in" *green*. Her husband, an electrician, then chimed in to say that the builders he worked for were developing houses that were energy efficient with incredibly low energy bills. After I gave them a simple overview of the six elements of green building, they quickly agreed that it was better to build green than to build traditionally. It seemed that this couple started out with the wrong impression of green building but could be quickly educated about its benefits.

When discussing green building, even with someone in the same profession, it is important to make sure that you are all on the same page. If you begin by asking the other person how he or she defines *green*, you will quickly learn how different people perceive this concept. When teaching a class, I once asked a classroom full of appraisers what they thought about green houses, and many of them unanimously answered "ugly." After questioning them as to why they defined *green* this way, it became apparent that they did not have a true understanding of green building. They had visions of houses of unusual styles covered in huge solar panels. If that is your view of green, it does not apply to most green

What is your definition of a green building, or, better yet, what is your client's view of green building?

structures. The ugliness these appraisers associated with green houses could just as easily apply to houses built in a conventional manner.

Exhibit 1.1 includes photographs of high-performance houses and non-green houses. Houses 1 and 3 are high-performance houses. House 1 has a solar thermal water heating system on the front that might be a clue to green but is not a dead giveaway. These are good examples of high-performance houses that do not necessarily have unusual styles.

The Six Elements of Green Building

The basic elements of green building are always the best place to begin any discussion of green building. An understanding of these six elements will help us see areas of importance that are not emphasized in the traditional code-built house, which will be referred to as *non-green* housing. (In this book, *non-green* housing is synonymous with *conventional-built, code-built,* or *traditional-built* housing.)

The six elements of green building are:

- Site
- Water efficiency
- Energy efficiency
- Indoor air quality

| Exhibit 1.1 | Can You Identify the High-Performance Houses? |

House 1

House 2

House 3

House 4

Green building takes a "whole building approach" by bringing together all the parties involved, from pre-design to completion, to implement a plan for a house in which the parts work together to result in high performance. This process often includes what is known as a *cradle-to-grave analysis*, which is a term used in life-cycle analysis to describe the entire life of a material or product up to the point of disposal. (It also refers to a system that handles a product from creation through disposal.) The "cradle" is the design phase of the project, and the "grave" phase encompasses what will happen to the building upon deconstruction or at the end of its physical life. For example, will the construction materials be recycled or moved to a landfill? A related term is *cradle-to-cradle analysis*, which describes the analysis of a material or product that is recycled. In this case, materials are reborn when they are recycled.*

Consider the following example of cradle-to-grave analysis. Most community residents do not want a landfill in their backyards. So in whose backyard should we place the landfill, or how will we reduce the need for more landfills? High-performance housing addresses this concern. Reducing the needed landfill space will increase public awareness about how high-performance housing benefits the entire community rather than just individual homeowners. The accompanying photo shows the Zemel Road Landfill in Charlotte County, Florida, where the cost and concern for environmental impact and future needs were considered. This landfill is a prime example of cradle-to-grave analysis in action.

According to an article in the *Charlotte Sun* written by the manager of Charlotte County Solid Waste Operations, the Zemel Road Landfill is the only one of its kind in the county.[†] The original land purchase was 100 acres with an additional 190 acres for future expansion. The landfill is expected to serve the needs of the county, based on projected population trends, until 2066. The solid waste division partnered with the county utility company to use dewatered domestic sludge as landfill cover. The sludge is mixed with yard waste and used to cover the garbage buried in the landfill, helping to reduce the use of purchased soil. Burying waste is the least expensive method of handling refuse. This landfill is self-supporting using tipping fees. It discourages but accepts out-of-county trash. Florida adopted a statewide recycling goal of 75% by the year 2020. The larger the number of residents who recycle, the longer the life of the landfill.

A Florida landfill on the cutting edge of waste management.

High-performance structures are built from materials that avoid creating more waste that will create more costs for future generations. Landfills add costs to households in the form of tax dollars used for purchasing land and covering maintenance expenses (such as expenses used for non-self-supporting landfills or to remedy the contamination of surrounding soils). Although this landfill is self-supporting now, it may not always be. Think of the alternative uses of 190 acres of land and you will begin to appreciate the cradle-to-grave or cradle-to-cradle analysis of green building.

* City of Seattle Office of Sustainability and Environment Green Building Glossary, www.seattle.gov/dpd/GreenBuilding/Resources/Greenbuildingglossary.
† Richard Allen, "County Landfill on Cutting Edge of Waste Management," *Charlotte Sun* (December 22, 2010): OT-11.

- Materials
- Operations and maintenance

These elements should work together in a high-performance structure. A truly green building has characteristics that relate to all six elements. Many houses may have one or more characteristics of a green building, but without all six elements a building does not qualify for most green building labels. For buildings that only have a few green features, it is more appropriate to identify the green characteristics without attaching the green label. The green-certifying raters offer expertise in verifying the green attributes that agents and real estate appraisers rely on in marketing and valuation. Appraisers and sales agents should be able to identify green characteristics, but they are not expected to have the same knowledge that green raters have in verifying and rating green structures.

Keeping the six elements of green building in mind during a site visit provides a competent appraiser with documentation to describe the property and apply valuation tools to develop value. Take the example of a house that was not certified as green but has characteristics reflecting all six elements of green. Appraising this house would test the appraiser's knowledge of high-performance building construction and design. A good example is a house I appraised that was built in 1989, before local green certifying organizations were formed. An architect designed the home to be energy efficient, low maintenance, and healthy. (The home was built for the architect's aging parents.) However, no one present during the site visit identified the green features (which I will describe later), and the client was surprised when I asked if the house was a green structure. All of the green features I noticed during the site visit were pieces of the puzzle that fit together to make a green building.

Site is the first element of green. I first noticed the site elements that fit with green standards in the driveway of this architect-designed home. The house had a desirable north-south orientation, a 5-foot overhang, and a minimal number of windows and doors on the east-west sides to maximize the energy efficiency of the building.

Water efficiency is the second element of green that was evident from the exterior of the house.

Exhibit 1.2   Fitting the Puzzle Pieces Together

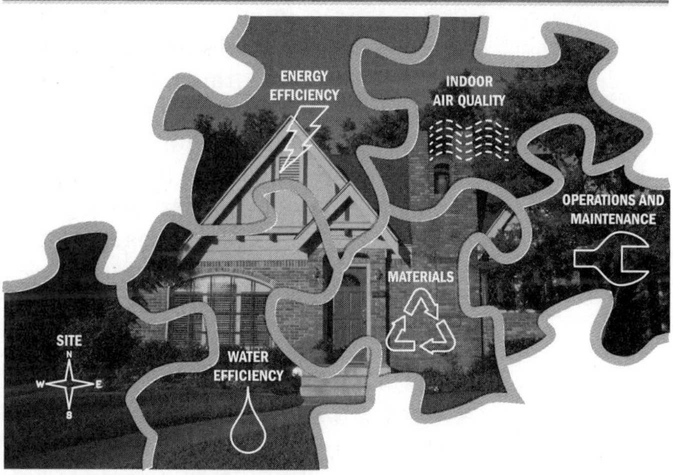

Storm water runoff drained into a 10,000-gallon cistern that could be used for fire protection or to water the lawn. Having a cistern for yard watering is an important feature in a market that has extremely high water rates and water restrictions and will not allow wells. This feature should be highlighted in the marketing of this sort of property.

Energy efficiency, the third element of green building, became evident when I viewed the interior, orientation, and comfort level inside this house on a hot day without the air-conditioning running. I asked the owner, "What is the average utility bill for this house?" It was much less than the expense for most houses of comparable size in the neighborhood.

Indoor air quality, the fourth element, is hard to identify without understanding the materials used in construction. A good sense of smell comes in handy when testing for this element. A green structure with green furnishings does not smell of materials that can be harmful to occupants. This structure had been closed because it was not occupied at the time, but it was furnished. The smell of stale air or volatile organic compounds (VOCs) was not evident.

Materials, the fifth element, are another part of green building that plays a role in quality, sustainability, and durability. Stone countertops, tile floors, solid wood doors and cabinetry, and good-quality windows are all green materials.

Operations and maintenance, the sixth element, is one that plays a role in the true cost of ownership. Building a structure that will last requires preventative maintenance of the mechanicals to avoid costly repairs in the future. The age of this house was not evident, and no major repairs were required.

By putting together all the pieces of the green building puzzle, I was able to support my opinion that the structure included all the elements of a green building, even though it was not formally certified or even considered to be a green structure by the owners.

Site

Site has a direct impact on the performance of a structure. An informed site review by all parties involved in the design that considers features such as orientation, drainage, environmental issues, view, trees, solar access, and linkages to public transportation, employers, shopping, and other neighborhood amenities should result in the correct placement of the structure on the site and the appropriate design of improvements for maximum performance. (A commonly used quantitative measure of the strength of a site's linkages with surrounding amenities is the Walk Score, available online at www.walkscore.com.) Not every site can have perfect physical and locational characteristics, but the weaknesses can be minimized with appropriate planning. Building the right structure on the site will result in benefits for many years to come.

Case Study: Green Housing and Site Characteristics
The following case study demonstrates the importance of site characteristics and benefits that apply to building design and orientation.

The property is a 45-unit development of Spanish-style villas that all have the same square footage and floor plan. The development is largely occupied by senior citizens. The all-electric units were built within a two-year period using the same set of specifications. The major differences in the villas include number of skylights, window type, mature tree location, orientation on the site, and a 500-sq.-ft. porch that is either screened or glass-enclosed with a split-unit heat and air system. The units with enclosed porches add conditioned space that changes the total conditioned space measurement from 2,000 square feet to 2,500 square feet.

This development is located in southwest Florida, where air-conditioning is typically used at least nine months out of the year. The average occupant keeps the thermostat at 76 degrees in the summer months and 70 in the winter months. These units were built between 1989 and 1990, when green construction was not evident in this market.

This is a perfect development for studying the effect that orientation can have on the utility bill. This study includes units that were occupied year-round by two adults each, all with similar lifestyles. Exhibit 1.3 shows a summary of the findings.

Unit 1 has the lowest monthly utility costs of the units studied. Its orientation, location of a mature oak tree, low-emissivity ("low-E") windows, energy-efficient light fixtures, standard electric water heater with timer, and compact fluorescent lamps (CFLs) account for its major differences from the other units. Three large skylights exposed to the south have solar shades that allow light to enter but block UV rays and additional heat.

The west side of this unit has no exposure to the sun because the west wall is shared with the adjacent unit. The north side of the building has a 32-ft. wall of low-E windows. The mature oak tree shades the south side of the building, which has one 52-by-44-in. window and two 12-by-44-in. windows. The east side of the building has four small windows and one 53-by-44-in. window. Therefore, this unit benefits from its orientation, energy-efficient features, and landscaping. The air-conditioning unit is original and not high

Unit 1

Exhibit 1.3   Description of Residential Living Units

Feature	Unit 1	Unit 2	Unit 3	Unit 4	Unit 5	Unit 6
Orientation (front-rear)	South-north	South-north	North-south	North-south	East-west	East-west
Conditioned space (sq. ft.)	2,500	2,500	2,000	2,500	2,000	2,000
Skylights	5, facing south and north	5, facing south and north	5, facing north and south	5, facing north and south	8, facing east and west	5, facing east and west
Landscape	Mature oak, south side	Mature oak, south side	No mature trees	Mature oak, north side	Mature oak, east side	No mature trees
Shading on skylights	Solar shades on south skylights	Solar shades on north-south skylights	No	No	No	No
New high-efficiency air-conditioner	No—original 13 SEER* for 2,000 sq. ft. and new split unit for 500 sq. ft.	Newer high-efficiency central air	No	Not at time of survey but reported bill lowered $20 per month after installing new unit	New air and furnace installed 4 years ago	No
Timer on water heater	Yes	No	No	No	No	No
New low-emissivity windows	Yes	Yes	No	No	No	No
New Energy Star light fixtures	Yes—all with CFLs	Yes—some with CFLs	No	No	No	No
Average monthly utility costs	$63	$85	$100	$127	$114	$128

* Seasonal Energy Efficiency Ratio, as defined by the Air Conditioning, Heating, and Refrigeration Institute. The US Department of Energy's established minimum SEER rating for cooling is 13 (www.ari.org/terms+and+technical+definitions.aspx).

efficiency. The split unit in the enclosed porch is a three-year-old, energy-efficient unit.

Unit 2 has the second-lowest bill in the dataset because of its orientation, location of mature oak tree, low-E windows, newer high-efficiency air-conditioning unit, solar shades on the large skylight areas, and energy-efficient light fixtures. This unit does not have CFLs or a timer on its electric water heater. The south side of this unit benefits from the shade of a mature oak tree. The east side does not have exposure to the morning sun because the east wall is shared with the adjacent unit. The north side of the unit is a 32-ft. window wall of low-E windows, and the west side has four small low-E windows and one 53-in.-wide, low-E window. This unit benefits from its orientation, energy-efficient features, and landscaping.

The electric bill of Unit 3 falls in the middle of the range. The south side of this unit is exposed to the sun and therefore keeps the living room and master bedroom at higher temperatures. The west side of this unit is somewhat shaded by the unit next door and has four small windows and one 53-in.-wide window. The east wall has no sun exposure because it is a common wall. This unit does not have low-E windows, newer HVAC, mature oak shading, or a water heater timer. The unit has more exposure to the sun on the south side and does not have the advantage of landscape shading.

The electric bill of Unit 4 falls in the upper end of the range. The south side of this unit is exposed to the sun, which keeps the living room and master bedroom at higher temperatures. The west side of this unit is somewhat shaded by the next-door unit and has four small windows and a 53-in.-wide window. The east wall has no sun exposure because it is a common wall. This unit does not have low-E windows, newer HVAC, or a water heater timer. This unit has more exposure to the sun. The owner reports that a new high-efficiency air-conditioner was installed after this survey, which lowered the electric bill by about $20 per month.

The electric bill of Unit 5 is in the mid-range of the dataset. The west side of the building has exposure to the full afternoon sun through a 32-ft. wall of windows. The windows are not low-E. The furnace and air-conditioning unit were replaced four years ago. The tree on the east side shades the unit from the morning sun. The south side of this unit has four small windows, one 53-in.-wide window, and some shading from the adjacent building. The north wall is a common wall with the adjacent unit. This unit has more skylights than the other units, which add additional heat if shading is not used during peak sun hours. The skylights on the east and west sides are exposed to the morning and afternoon sun.

Unit 6 has the highest bill of the dataset. The west side of the building has exposure to the full afternoon sun through a 32-foot wall of windows. The windows are not low-E. The furnace and air conditioning unit were replaced recently. The south side of this unit has four small windows, one 53-in.-wide window, and no shading. The north wall is shared with the adjacent unit. The skylights are exposed to the morning and afternoon sun on the east and west sides. The orientation and lack of shading are responsible for the higher utility costs in this unit.

This example clearly suggests that the unit with the lowest utility bill has energy-efficient upgrades, a mature oak tree, and good orientation, which are the major contributors to low costs. The unit with the highest utility bills has limited energy upgrades and an orientation that needs better landscaping in order to provide shade.

Surprisingly, the energy costs for these units were not mentioned in the marketing of the units, which were sold in the past five years. Some observers might question the use of a development with senior occupants in a study of influences on energy expenses because seniors often conserve energy by adjusting the thermostat setting and may not use heat or air-conditioning until the weather is extreme. However, the units studied displayed similar occupant behavior and thus provide a real measure of the structure's performance rather than the conservation habits of the occupants.

Sales agents with knowledge of high-performance buildings and the ability to market and articulate value to buyers can greatly assist the market's perception of high-performance houses. Agents are instrumental in educating the public about the desirability of real estate, and they must be fully informed of all property features that have a value benefit. The agent's ability to communicate the value of energy-efficient or high-performance features can influence the price paid and better serve the interests of the parties to the transaction.

The following issues affecting the market value of high-performance houses are evident in this example:

- If the property is not marketed in a manner that highlights those features that affect the monthly budget as well as the comfort of the occupants, how are buyers supposed to make informed decisions? Why would buyers pay more if they are not informed of the economic benefits of a property that save them money each month? Omitting this economic benefit in marketing suggests that it does not have value, at least in the eyes of the sellers.
- If there is no evidence that properties with sustainable features sell for a premium or experience a shorter marketing period, there may be no support for attaching a premium. The market determines value by the prices paid. Builders, agents, and owners who sell a high-performance house at the same price as the alternative code-built house may be unwittingly contributing to comparative market values for high-performance homes that do not reflect the additional value they should command over code-built houses.
- Appraisers are sometimes criticized for undervaluing property rights. However, an appraiser must study and measure market performance. Market participants–including buyers, sellers, contractors, and sales agents–all have a role in understanding and communicating the extent to which sustainable features are or are not part of the transaction decision. Appraisers use the results of that data to develop market value. Appraisers do not determine value; the market determines value.

Water Efficiency

Water efficiency is one of two measurable elements of green building that affect the homeowner's monthly budget. Potable water is an expensive and diminishing commodity in many areas.

With appropriate planning and research, water costs can be greatly reduced. Water efficiency is accomplished through the use of cisterns, rain barrels, low- or zero-water landscaping, and water-efficient fixtures such as low-flow showerheads. Waste water from kitchen, bathroom, and laundry sinks, tubs, and washers, known as *gray water*, can be reused for landscaping. However, not all local governments allow water recycling. Low-flow toilets, showerheads, and fixtures that conserve water make a major difference in water use and are required in many areas.

Energy Efficiency

A home's energy efficiency is another measureable element of green building that can assist in the marketing and valuing of residential properties. Energy efficiency obviously affects the monthly budget.

Most homeowners know the amounts of their monthly energy bills because those bills arrive on a regular basis for the full term of their use and ownership of the property. The owner of a green house that performs better and uses less energy than a non-green house could easily calculate the amount of money saved over the term of ownership. However, the market determines whether that cost savings would be worth a premium at the time of purchase and at the time of sale. The appraiser studies the market and, in the appraisal report, describes the behavior of participants in terms of prices paid. Interviewing buyers and sellers in the market assists appraisers in understanding what was and was not considered in their buying decisions.

For example, consider that much of the energy efficiency gains currently achieved in high-performance housing are a result of easy adaptations that add approximately 5% to the base price per square foot of construction. This estimate is based on costs reported in the Marshall & Swift/Boeckh *Residential Cost Handbook* for a structure in a moderate climate as shown in Exhibit 1.4. (The *Residential Cost Handbook* considers a superinsulated structure to include an extreme climate package for windows, stud walls that can be double 2-by-4s or 2-by-8s, and R-30 wall insulation with an air infiltration wrap and up to R-55 ceiling insulation.[1]) The base price considers a moderate climate cost for insulation. The additional costs, which change with the climate or region, are typically between 3.5% and 5.4%.

Exhibit 1.4	Adjustment to Base Price for Superinsulation		
Structure Size/ Avg. Quality	Sq. Ft. Costs Prior to Adjustment	Additional $/Sq. Ft. to Superinsulate	% Increase Attributed to Energy Adj.
1,200-sq.-ft. stud frame/wood siding	$84.22	$4.22	5% ($4.22/$84.22)
1,900-sq.-ft. stud frame/wood siding	$77.16	$4.22	5.4% ($4.22/$77.16)

Source: *Residential Cost Handbook* (Milwaukee, WI: Marshall & Swift/Boeckh, 2012).

As the earlier example clearly indicated, a residence's site has an effect on energy use within the structure. The site must be considered in the design of the structure in order to enhance energy efficiency. For example, strategically positioned trees can conserve up to 25% of the amount of energy a typical household uses.[2]

One way efficiency is achieved within a structure is by tightening the thermal envelope of the building to avoid unconditioned air infiltrating the interior conditioned space. The components of the building envelope are the roof, walls, windows, doors, and foundation; in other words, the envelope is everything that divides the indoor and outdoor environments. In some construction types, the envelope would stop at the ceiling rather than the roof, so the space between

---

1. The insulation R-value measures the resistance to heat flow.
2. US Department of Energy, "Landscaping for Energy Efficient Homes," http://energy.gov/energysaver/articles/landscaping-energy-efficient-homes.

the roof and the outer surface of the ceiling would be inside the building's structure but outside the envelope. Of course, some construction types might condition the attic. Creating a "tight" envelope, insulating properly, and using energy-efficient windows, mechanicals, and light fixtures results in a structure with a lower utility bill. A tightly built structure requires a mechanical system to move air as needed from the exterior to the interior, but the flow of air is controlled to maximize efficiency and avoid creating other functional problems.

With 50% or more of a house's energy costs devoted to heating and cooling, replacing and repairing ducts can be an important strategy for spending less money on energy, saving anywhere from 20% to 40% on home heating and cooling costs. A Duct Blaster is used to measure the tightness of ducts and determine if repairs are needed. This measurement is usually reported as a cubic feet per minute (CFM) rating. Leakage is not a concern for ducts installed in the conditioned space.

Water heating can raise a monthly utility bill significantly, but that expense can be lowered by other simple measures such as installing an inexpensive timer on the water heater. Another easy way to reduce water heating costs is to reduce the temperature of the water in the heater by a few degrees. Cranking up the heat takes energy, and that energy costs money every time the burner in the water tank ignites to maintain the temperature of the hot water in the house. In some cases, an insulated blanket may be needed to conserve heated water. Other measures might include using tankless or solar thermal watering heating systems, which have higher installation costs but low operating costs. Incentives are often available for energy-efficient water heating systems.[3]

Exhibit 1.5 shows the breakdown of energy use in American homes in 2010 according to the US Department of Energy. While the data from the various sources compiled for this study varies slightly, all agree that the largest costs for energy are attributable to space heating, air conditioning, and water heating. The areas of highest energy expenditures would logically be the areas to emphasize in a building improvement designed to maximize the structure's performance. Appraisers should carefully consider the categories shown on this chart when inspecting a property when describing energy features. Many existing homes have energy upgrades that should be acknowledged. However, having one or more of these features does not automatically make a home green.

Some insurance companies offer a guaranteed energy usage program for the two-year period after the homeowner purchases a new home. If a home exceeds its guaranteed usage at the end of the year, the guarantee provider will pay the difference. When builders purchase guarantees like this, they demonstrate confidence in the energy-

---

3.   Residential Energy Services Network, "Your Ducts Could Be Costing You Money!" and "How to Control Water Heating Costs," www.resnet.us/library.

efficient features of the homes they build. Examples of residential energy guarantee programs include the following:

- SystemVision (www. advancedenergy.org/ portal/systemvision) SystemVision was launched in 2000 and is sponsored by the North Carolina Housing Finance Agency (NCHFA) in partnership with Advanced Energy. As of July 20, 2013, the number of affordable homes with energy bills guaranteed by this program was 3,773.[4]

- Bonded Builders Warranty Group (www.bondedbuilders.com/builders/ residential-energy-guarantee) Bonded Builders Warranty Group offers builders a Residential Energy Guarantee for two, three, or five years based on the projection of a home's total energy use in a Home Energy Rating System (HERS) report.[5] Bonded Builders Warranty Group will pay participating homeowners for any additional annual natural gas and electric cost over the HERS projection. Special pricing options are available for homes certified by the National Green Building Standard (NGBS).

These types of programs should be mentioned in the appraisal report and on any supplementary documentation such as the Appraisal Institute's Residential Green and Energy Efficient Addendum, which will be discussed more in Chapter 6. Appraisers should research the details of the guarantee to see if the guarantee can be transferred with the home. In some cases, the guarantee stays with the home over a designated period of time. If a guarantee is transferred, it

Exhibit 1.5   Energy Use in US Households, 2010

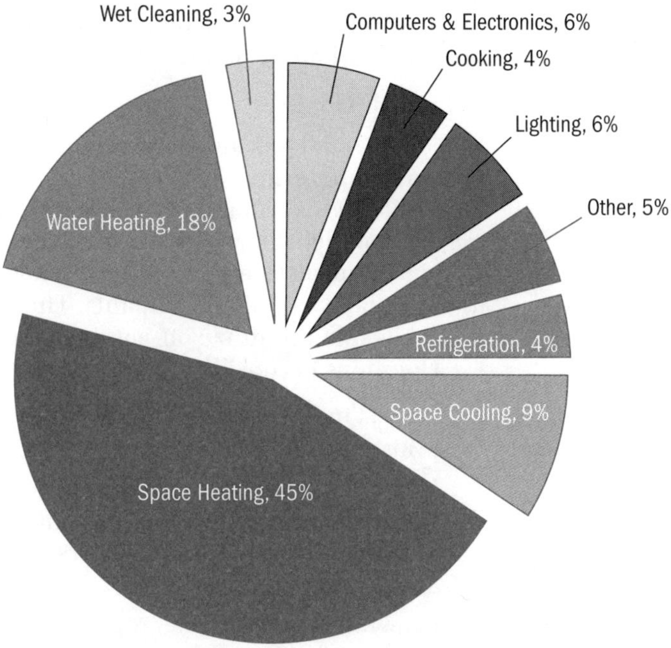

Wet Cleaning, 3%
Computers & Electronics, 6%
Cooking, 4%
Lighting, 6%
Other, 5%
Refrigeration, 4%
Space Cooling, 9%
Space Heating, 45%
Water Heating, 18%

Source: US Department of Energy, "Tips on Saving Money and Energy at Home," http://energy.gov/sites/prod/files/2013/06/f2/energy_savers.pdf.

---

4. SystemVision by Advanced Energy, "Developer's Guide," www.advancedenergy.org/buildings/ affordable_housing/systemvision/wp-content/uploads/downloads/2012/01/ SV_DeveloperGuide.pdf.

5. *Builder Magazine* (published by the National Association of Home Builders) (September 2013): 92. Note that the HERS Index is the industry standard for measuring a home's energy efficiency and will be discusssed in greater detail later in this book. More information on the HERS Index is available at www.resnet.us/hers-index.

should be listed in the multiple listing service (MLS) in a searchable data field. Appraisers cannot adequately analyze the effect that the guarantee may have on the home if the relevant databases do not provide searchable fields.

Indoor Air Quality

Indoor air quality is an element of green building that may not be easy to measure in terms of dollars, but it is something that is appreciated by a building's occupants every day. With most people spending the majority of their time indoors, this element should be a concern for all. Mechanical systems used in a structure can produce off-gassing that may be harmful to occupants. Therefore, using mechanicals and materials that minimize off-gassing results in better indoor air quality.

Questions to consider about indoor air quality include the following:

- Why is indoor air quality next to impossible to value in the appraisal process?
- How many databases such as multiple listing services, public property records, or other commercial databases offer a searchable field that allows appraisers or the public to search for indoor air quality features?
- How many sales agents report that buyers are seeking houses with good indoor air quality?

Clearly no one would want poor indoor air quality in a building that he or she is going to occupy, and good indoor air quality can positively affect the health and comfort of the occupants. Poor indoor air quality is likely to result in additional medical expense. More people are experiencing asthma, lung, and allergy problems than ever before. These health problems are aggravated by volatile organic compounds (VOCs), which are chemicals found in cleaning products, paints, and other household items that can affect indoor air quality and occupant health and safety.[6] Indoor air quality can be enhanced by using low-VOC materials, tightening the building envelope to prevent dust and outdoor odors from infiltrating the interior living area, and using indoor air quality filters and mechanicals. The same care should be given to the furnishings. When the envelope is tightly sealed, a carbon dioxide or radon monitor is often installed with the ventilation system. Innovative pest management techniques that seal access using nonchemical baiting reduce the use of pesticides that are harmful to indoor air quality.

To experience the importance of indoor air quality for yourself, tour a house that is not built green and one that is built green. Do you notice a difference in the way the homes smell? Non-green homes often smell like a new car, but green homes should not, assuming that the furnishings are also green.

Indoor air quality is an element of green building that appraisers may not be able to measure in market value, but it is an element that homeowners cannot afford to ignore.

---

6. *Building Science Principles Reference Guide*, 1st ed. (Malta, NY: Building Performance Institute, 2012), 253.

Materials

The materials element of green building affects indoor air quality, physical life, energy efficiency, carbon footprint, and building costs. Recycled materials are used in green structures when possible. However, recycled materials are not necessarily lower in quality or cost as compared to non-recycled materials. The use of recyclable materials and materials that are manufactured within 500 miles of the job site may result in green points toward a green certification. The use of recyclable materials ensures that, upon deconstruction of the home, the materials will not be required to end up in the waste stream or a dump, which will affect future land use in the community. For example, Hurricane Charlie provided Florida homeowners and real estate professionals alike with a lesson in 2004 when the storm devastated communities and the streets were filled with construction materials that were later transported to a landfill.

Using locally sourced materials helps the local economy. Staying within 500 miles of the job site keeps the carbon footprint and transportation costs lower. It may not be possible to use materials from within 500 miles of the job site, but that would not mean that the house could not receive a green certification. The certification process takes into consideration all elements of green. Most certifying organizations have prerequisites and minimum points in each category.

The materials used in a structure affect the appraisal process in many ways. First of all, the application of the cost approach includes the analysis of physical life estimates and material costs. Materials also affect energy efficiency and indoor air quality. They may also affect market appeal, just as they do for conventional-built housing, and would thus be considerations in market analysis, highest and best use analysis, and the sales comparison approach.

Operations and Maintenance

A home's operations and maintenance affect the homeowner's budget and free time. Building smarter is the key to spending less time and money on operations and maintenance.

Green building technology should result in houses that are more comfortable to occupy, have fewer repairs, and therefore cost less to maintain. Houses that do not perform at a high level have symptoms that may include mold, rotting wood, ice dams, peeling paint, and many other costly or time-consuming maintenance problems. Houses that do not perform well or that show signs of deferred maintenance are likely to be penalized by the market in terms of price and marketing time. Green building technology does not guarantee a maintenance-free house, but it should result in less maintenance overall. Green builders usually provide an owner's operation manual and some education on the maintenance of the new structure. Following these guidelines results in a longer life span for the structure and less maintenance cost over time.

Green Certifications

A true green building has the characteristics of all six green building elements. A building that is certified as green has verification from a third-party green rater that the building has met the guidelines of a particular green building program. Not all green buildings are certified, but that does not necessarily make them less green. Green certifications do add additional soft costs to construction, but many buyers choose certification as a means of ensuring that the house meets the green label characteristics. Some buyers seek the name recognition of the green label for bragging rights just as they would with designer clothing and luxury cars.

During the appraisal process, appraisers value the property's physical, economic, and locational characteristics, rather than the certification. Therefore, if a building built to the green standard does not have a green certification, it should still be valued based on its high-performance construction characteristics. The appraiser must have competency in green construction to value non-certified green buildings appropriately. (Appraiser competency will be addressed in detail in Chapter 3.)

Comparing green certifying organizations' ratings is difficult because there are more than 100 certifying organizations in the United States. While many people think that green certification organizations are national, most of these organizations operate at the regional level. The national green certification organizations include:

- The US Green Building Council (USGBC), which promotes the Leadership in Energy and Environmental Design (LEED) certification

- Home Innovation Research Labs, which provides green certification to the National Green Building Standard (NGBS)

- The ICC 700 National Green Building Standard, adopted by the National Association of Home Builders (NAHB) and the International Code Council (ICC) and approved by the American National Standards Institute (ANSI)

- Energy Star, which only grants certifications for energy efficiency, water efficiency, and indoor air quality elements

Appraisers and sales agents do not certify or provide certifications for green buildings. Third-party certifiers must be relied on for documents and certification ratings. A third-party certification should be included in the appraisal report and attached to the MLS listing to provide clear information to the users of valuation services.

All Green Certifications Are Not Equal

Appraisers, real estate agents, builders, and the public need to have an understanding of the different certification processes and a comparative view of the different rating systems. Because there are over 100 green building certification organizations, comparing the ratings from a national perspective is next to impossible. These various organizations use different categories, worksheets, performance testing, point systems, and certification names. However, they all measure one or more of the six green building elements in their rating systems. Therefore, if real estate professionals can identify the six elements of green building and know the programs administered by the green organizations that are prevalent in their market areas, they will be well prepared to address green building issues.

Home inspection companies, which provide a service to homebuyers by verifying the working condition of certain features of a home, are also beginning to offer green certifications for existing homes. Keep in mind that home inspectors provide a different type of service than appraisers. Appraisers should review the worksheets prepared by home inspection companies carefully to understand the rating system used because not all green certifications are equal. For example, we can compare the green worksheets available on the Move-In Certified website (www.moveincertified.com/green) to the green worksheets used by other green organizations. The Move-In certification does not include a HERS Index rating or Duct Blaster test as part of the inspection. Instead, the worksheet only calls for the inspector's observations on a series of items. Sales agents listing properties with this type of green certification should be extremely clear about the type of inspection performed.

Inaccurate or misleading MLS listings that indicate a green certification without specifying the certification type could create problems. For example, an appraiser might use MLS data of a green certification prepared by a home inspector thinking that the certification meets the same criteria as the LEED certification. This could result in an inaccurate value conclusion due to misleading data or a lack of verification by the appraiser.

Sales agents and appraisers must become familiar with the green certifying organizations prevalent in their markets. Having a copy of the certification worksheet for each organization is helpful to understanding the differences between ratings. Obtaining a copy of the owner's or builder's application for certification will help you with documenting high-performance features.

It is important for appraisers to keep in mind the vital roles they play in educating the public on various real estate features and helping market participants make good decisions.

Documentation for Efficiency Upgrades

The Building Performance Institute (BPI) develops technical standards, certifications, accreditations, and related technical documents to support the safe and effective improvement of energy performance in existing residential buildings, including multifamily properties. Their document, *BPI-2101-S-2013 Standard Requirements for a Certificate of Completion for Residential Energy Upgrades* (available at www.bpi.org), defines the new efficiency programs rolling out across the country. Note that according to these requirements, the efficiency improvements made on existing homes should be documented in a format similar to that of the Appraisal Institute's Residential Green and Energy Efficient Addendum.

ADDITIONAL RESOURCES

Green Building Technology

The following websites offer free short videos and other informative resources to help you enhance your knowledge of green building technology:

· Home Energy Pros: http://homeenergypros.lbl.gov

· GreenExpo 365: www.greenexpo365.com

· 50 Green: www.50Green.com

Home Energy Costs

The EPA website includes a downloadable document, *Energy Savers: Tips on Saving Money and Energy at Home*, that can help you gain a better understanding of home energy costs and ways of lowering these costs. The document can be found at http://energy.gov/sites/prod/files/2013/06/f2/energy_savers.pdf.

Documentation for Efficiency Upgrades

The Building Performance Institute (BPI) develops technical standards, certifications, accreditations, and related technical documents to support the safe and effective improvement of energy performance in existing residential buildings, including multifamily properties. Their document, *BPI-2101-S-2013 Standard Requirements for a Certificate of Completion for Residential Energy Upgrades* defines the new efficiency programs rolling out across the country. Note that the efficiency improvements made on an existing home are documented in a format that will fit into the Appraisal Institute's Residential Green and Energy Efficient Addendum. *Standard Requirements for a Certificate of Completion for Residential Energy Upgrades* can be found at www.bpi.org.

MLS TIPS

· The indoor air quality features of a building are often hidden in other fields of the listing, such as "Interior Features," "Exterior Features," or "Foundation Details."

· The Real Estate Standards Organization (RESO) publishes a *Data Dictionary* that includes a recommended green search field called "Green Energy Efficiency." Within that field, including an additional menu option titled "Incentives and Other" is recommended. Appraisers can consult this dictionary to learn tips on how to search the fields to extract relevant data. RESO develops, promotes, and maintains voluntary electronic commerce standards for the real estate finance industry (www.reso.org).

The Challenges of Valuing Green

The definition of *green* detailed in the previous chapter is just a starting point for discussing high-performance residences. Even if a property has met the definition of *green* and has a third-party certification to back up that claim, the appraiser must still determine exactly how green the property is. The specific "shade of green" of a property is related to its green rating or score established by the certifying organization. A rating near the top of the range of available points would reflect a "dark shade" of green and may indicate that the property cost more to build because of its additional features. A lower score would indicate a "lighter shade" of green.

With more than 100 rating organizations in the United States using different rating methods and system names, comparing the ratings is next to impossible. Appraisers should become familiar with the green rating organizations that are most prevalent in their area. Most organizations provide information on their ratings system or at least contact information on their websites. The diversity of rating organizations is one of the major problems appraisers encounter when trying to compare shades of green in a meaningful way during the valuation process. Standardization of the green ratings would allow buyers and sellers to make better-informed decisions and would simplify the valuation process. However, it is unlikely that one rating organization will evolve and emerge from the competing alternatives given the investment each organization has already made in its own rating system.

Compounding the process of valuing the shades of green is the difficulty appraisers experience in finding information about green features in the databases they currently use. Appraisers most often refer to local multiple listing services when conducting residential appraisals. Unfortunately, the green fields in MLS databases are not being populated completely or correctly, and the shade of green is not a standard searchable field in most systems.

Market Data Problems

Analysis of market data in some areas may reveal that the market is willing to pay a premium for particular green labels, such as a LEED certification. However, appraisers must measure each market carefully to develop credible values for green buildings, and measuring the market requires good databases with green fields that are accurately populated.

It bears repeating that appraisers do not determine value. Rather, the market determines the prices paid for properties, and appraisers develop values based on those reported market prices. The major problem in valuing high-performance houses derives directly from the appraiser's dependence on the market; a lack of data means a lack of support for the value contributions of green attributes. Databases are years behind the green building movement, especially considering that green building has actually been around in its modern form since the 1970s. Multiple listing services are making great strides in adding green fields to their databases. The Green MLS Tool Kit (www.greenthemls.org) is one real estate industry collaborative project dedicated to this goal. Also, MLS organizations owned and operated by local Realtor associations were mandated to comply with the Real Estate Transaction Standards (RETS) by June 2009 and to keep current with the standard's new versions by implementing new releases of RETS within one year of ratification.[1] However, there are between 10 and 15 different MLS software programs that serve MLS databases for various local Realtor associations. As of July 2013, 185 out of 850 MLS databases had searchable green data fields, according to Kristen Short, managing director of the green designation program of the National Association of Realtors (NAR). This association does not control the software system or fields used by each individual local association. However, until the NAR begins to monitor compliance, it may be years before nationwide compliance is implemented.

MLS data fields are intended to provide a basic description, but their primary purpose is for marketing. In many cases, term usage is not consistent from one listing to another. Appraisers and prospective buyers should perform their own due diligence. This challenge is more acute when it comes to properties that are built to sustainability standards. The use of the word *green* has marketing value, but it can be misleading if not outright inaccurate without a standard set of definitions or instructions provided by the listing agency.

"Apples and Oranges" Comparisons

Using existing databases in green valuation assignments presents many difficulties. For example, consider the case of an appraiser who searches the local MLS for all sales of green houses that sold within 12 months in one county. This search results in 30 sales identified as green. However, after the appraiser performed more research, she determined that only one out of these 30 sales was actually a green home.

---

1. National Association of Realtors, *2013 Handbook on Multiple Listing Policy*, Operational Issues, Section 12: Real Estate Transaction Standards (RETS), www.realtor.org/2013-handbook-on-multiple-listing-policy.

Consider what might happen when this appraiser, who most likely has only one or two days to visit a site and write an appraisal report, searches the MLS and does not verify those 30 sales with the parties involved in the transactions. (Keep in mind that using an MLS is considered to be using a source and not verifying data.) Because sales that are not green are inaccurately listed as "comparables" in the MLS database, no premium would be attributed for any elements of green construction.

Why is no value attributed to green houses in this case? It may be because the sales were not green properties but the appraiser assumed they were green based on their MLS listings. The appraiser might incorrectly assume that she is making an "apples to apples" comparison when comparing a subject property that she has confirmed is green at the site visit to comparable properties that are supposedly green based on the MLS data. Until green data in MLS databases is more reliable, appraisers will need more than just a couple of days to appropriately research data for a green valuation. The extended amount of time needed to research and develop a supported opinion of value deserves a higher appraisal fee, which usually is not awarded. A complex appraisal assignment deserves a competent appraiser, a sufficient amount of time for research and development, and a fee commensurate with the time involved in the assignment. In most cases, appraisers are not receiving sufficient fees to do the research necessary to value high-performance houses.

When appraisers interview sales agents, the two parties often speak two different languages and the truth does not emerge. In the verification process, appraisers must start with the basics and explain what they mean by *green*. If the agent and the appraiser define this term differently, misinformation usually results. Too often, data input is incorrect and negatively affects the valuation of high-performance houses.

Why would an agent list a property as green in the MLS when it is not? Interviews I have conducted have revealed the following reasons:

- Lack of green knowledge on the agent's part
- Misrepresentation of green on the seller's part
- An effort to draw as many potential buyers as possible by checking boxes for as many features as possible in the listing
- Inadequate documentation required by MLS boards before allowing the green boxes to be checked
- Inadequate penalties imposed by MLS boards for improperly representing a property as green

An MLS board that includes appraisers in the process of developing searchable green data fields should ensure that the system includes appropriate data fields for developing value. Although the main purpose of the MLS is marketing, it has an extremely important role in documenting value as well. Engaging appraisers in the discussion of searchable fields will benefit all property types and the public.

Markets without Green Sales Data

Sales of residences with green features are a new occurrence in many markets. What should an appraiser do when working in a market that lacks green comparable sales? Many practitioners have been asking this question, and the answers vary widely. Some underwriters suggest that limited or no green sales indicate that green features have no value. However, this argument cannot be applied to similar situations, such as the market standard changing from residences with two-car garages to those with three-car garages. The same underwriters who now insist on paired sales to accept an energy efficiency or green adjustment did not question a garage adjustment based on cost alone before sales of houses with three-car garages could be found in the market.

Appraisers report that representatives of institutions ordering appraisals for lending purposes have often told them to ignore green features and appraise green properties as if they were traditionally built. This would mean that the appraiser would not have to describe or value green features, and thus sales data would not be a problem. However, an appraiser who follows this advice would not be in compliance with the Uniform Standards of Professional Appraisal Practice (USPAP).

Following this type of direction would result in a misleading appraisal report that does not reflect the true physical and economic characteristics of the property, as referenced in Standards Rule 1-2 of the 2014-2015 edition of USPAP. But what is an appraiser to do when the client provides such instructions? Declining the assignment is always an option, and in some cases it may be the best response.

The Appraisal Practices Board (APB) of the Appraisal Foundation issued a first exposure draft of a valuation advisory titled *Valuation of Green Building: Background and Core Competency* in 2013. This advisory clearly addresses several potential issues that relate to the valuation of green buildings:

- Assigning value, or no value, to green components without market support
- Finding market support for influences on value, the difficulties encountered when using currently available database information, and the importance of culling green features from imperfect data
- Overlooking green features, which may happen if the appraiser is not aware of the right features to look for and the right questions to ask
- Using inappropriate adjustments that are not supported by paired-sales rent analysis, market interviews, secondary data, or third-party research

This advisory document also indicates that appraisers should consider energy savings from energy-efficiency upgrades in the valuation process and should conduct adequate market research to support the use of gross rent multipliers, discounted cash flow, or similar income-based valuation techniques.[2]

Private Databases

Many of the green certifying organizations have databases of all the properties they have rated, but most of those organizations consider this information to be private and not for public use. This makes it very hard for an appraiser to determine the rating for a sale listed in the MLS as green that does not have a "green score" or "shade" of green indicated. Perhaps the score or shade of green has not been addressed in some MLS systems as a searchable field because, with so many different green rating systems available, software developers have difficulty finding a data field that would work for all green programs. Attaching the green certification and score sheet to the MLS listing is one way to address the detail needed by appraisers.

Some examples of databases that are not available for public use include Home Innovation Research Labs and the US Green Building Council's green rating databases, the US Environmental Protection Agency and Department of Energy's databases, and the Residential Energy Services Network's database of houses with HERS Index ratings.

Finally, none of these databases are designed to interact with each other. Imagine how much money is spent on proprietary databases that could be extremely helpful to the real estate industry but are not accessible or capable of interacting with other similar databases.

Other Market Data Problems

The lack of information readily available to appraisers will continue to be a problem for years to come. Property assessors do not usually document green ratings and often do not detail solar photovoltaic (PV) systems. If building permits are required for solar PV systems, the permit documents and data might have details that could be accessed by appraisers.

How the Different Shades of Green Affect Value

Why should an appraiser care about shades of green? To get an idea of the answer to this question, consider the answer you would get if you were to ask a builder if it costs more to build a structure rated the darkest shade of green as compared to a structure with a lighter shade rating. Marshall and Swift/Boeckh's 2013 *Residential Cost Handbook* reports that the additional cost to build green instead of code ranges from 3% to 20%. This range is so wide because the shade of green is a determining factor.

If a structure costs more to build, the seller usually expects to sell it at a higher price. That often means that an appraisal is required. To develop the value of a home built to the darkest shade of green,

---

2.   Valuation of Green Buildings: Background and Core Competency, first exposure draft (Washington, D.C.: Appraisal Practices Board of The Appraisal Foundation, 2013).

appraisers need either sales of properties that are the same shade or data to support an adjustment for the different shades of green. This is where the problem lies, since most databases do not provide details such as the specific green rating.

Consider the additional work required of an appraiser when the shade of green is ignored in the readily available data. For example, an MLS search revealed 217 green house sales in one planned-unit development in 2012. This development is a green community with a green education center for the public. After downloading additional data to determine the shades of green that were in play, the appraiser discovered that the investigation would not be possible without major research. The MLS showed that the homes in the development were green-certified, but no ratings were provided. A search of the database of the local certifying organizations revealed only one property rating out of the 217 sales. Interviewing the team in the development's sales office (who were not sales agents) did not provide any results. Their response was that their houses had various shades of green, and they could not understand why the shade would be important. When asked if the sales prices were different based on the shade of green, they readily agreed that they were. However, even for this large number of green houses, there was insufficient data to develop a value opinion of the shades of green. While sales may be available, appraisers are severely handicapped by the limitations of databases and reporting methods.

Exhibit 2.1 lists the major factors that may influence sales prices and value opinions of high-performance properties. This list is not all-inclusive and only addresses features that may be attributed to high-performance houses. How many of these features are found on Form 1004 and used for mortgage lending purposes by government-sponsored entities such as Fannie Mae and Freddie Mac? Only the roof

---

Exhibit 2.1   High-Performance Property Features That May Affect Value

- Shade of green or label
  - Formally certified or no certification
- Energy features/HERS Index rating
  - Solar
  - Wind
  - Geothermal
  - Other renewables
  - Insulation type
- Materials used
  - Metal roof or asphalt shingle
- Water-efficient features
  - Cistern
  - Gray water reuse system

---

material is shown on Form 1004. Therefore, the Appraisal Institute's Residential Green and Energy Efficient Addendum or a supplementary narrative description must be used with Form 1004 to communicate an appraisal that clearly describes a high-performance house. This addendum will be discussed in more detail later in this book.

However, the situation is not completely bleak. Some counties are aggressive in their promotion of green construction. In these rare cases, building permit offices may have a data field to distinguish how many green permits were issued annually. This can be a good resource for documenting the green trends in the neighborhood section of an appraisal report.

Possible Solutions

Market participants clearly need to understand the various shades of green. If buyers are "colorblind" and the shades of green do not matter to them, values will be equal for all shades of green regardless of the cost. Builders and green-certifying organizations need to educate consumers on green features so that they can understand the differences between the shades of green. Real estate agents must also be educated on the various shades of green and what the differences mean to value or price paid. How can an agent convince a buyer that a green house has more value than a code-built house if the agent doesn't know the difference?

Taking a proactive approach to how data is stored is extremely important and unfortunately absent from today's market. Green-certifying organizations must open their databases to real estate professionals or connect them to public databases. If more data is made available, competent appraisers will be able to gather the information they need to provide credible value opinions of green versus non-green homes.

MLS TIP

If your local MLS does not include sufficient green fields, it is important to communicate the reasons for implementing green fields to the local MLS board members who make the decisions about software and data fields. Appraisers can provide valuable tips for making data fields more user friendly for developing data searches.

Competency Concerns

SITE   WATER   ENERGY   AIR QUALITY   MATERIALS   MAINTENANCE

Just as different people and organizations have different ideas about what *green* is, different people have different ideas about what an appraiser needs to know in order to be considered competent in valuing green buildings and residential properties. Professional standards set minimum guidelines for competent appraisal practice, while the major government-sponsored enterprises (GSEs) involved in residential real estate financing have their own, more stringent guidelines. Other stakeholders in the real estate market, such as state appraiser boards and appraisal management companies (AMCs), have their own ideas about competency.

Perspectives on Competency

Where does appraiser competency start? The Uniform Standards of Professional Appraisal Practice (USPAP) provide *minimum* guidelines for developing and communicating appraisals, while underwriting guidelines often exceed the minimum. GSEs such as Fannie Mae and Freddie Mac charge lenders with knowing USPAP and ensuring that all appraisals comply with it. However, it seems the charge is not always being met.

Did you know that the GSE and Federal Housing Administration (FHA) guidelines have a higher competency standard than USPAP? Fannie Mae's "Guidance for Lenders and Appraisers" fact sheet published in 2009 clearly states that the appraiser must be competent in valuing a particular property type *prior* to accepting the assignment.[1] This is further stated in the 2013 *Fannie Mae Selling Guide*, as reproduced in Exhibit 3.1.

Note that both the 2009 and 2013 versions of the *Selling Guide* support the concept of appraiser competency *prior* to accepting the assignment. This guide places responsibility on both the lender and appraiser prior to accepting the assignment. It seems clear that competency should be the first criteria for the lender's choice in appraisers.

In contrast, USPAP allows for appraiser competency to be gained *after* the assignment is accepted and certain steps are followed. The

---

1. Fannie Mae, "Guidance for Lenders and Appraisers" (April 2009), www.fanniemae.com/ content /fact_sheet/appraisal-guidance.pdf.

Exhibit 3.1   Fannie Mae Guidelines for Appraiser Selection

✓	Lender Responsibilities
	Lenders must obtain an independent, disinterested examination and valuation of the property that secures a mortgage sold to Fannie Mae
	Lenders must be aware of, and in full compliance with, state laws for licensing and certification of real estate appraisers.
	Lenders must use appraisers who: · are state-licensed and state-certified in accordance with the provisions of the Title XI of the Financial Institutions Reform, Recovery and Enforcement Act of 1989; · have the requisite knowledge required to perform a professional quality appraisal for the specific geographic location and particular property type; · have the requisite knowledge about, and access to, the necessary and appropriate data sources for the area in which the appraisal assignment is located.
	Appraisers who are not familiar with specific real estate markets may not have adequate information available to preform a reliable appraisal. Although the Uniform Standards of Professional Appraisal Practice (USPAP) allows an appraiser who does not have the appropriate knowledge and experience to accept an appraisal assignment by providing procedures with which the appraiser can complete the assignment, Fannie Mae requires a lender to only use an appraiser who has the appropriate knowledge and experience, and does not allow the USPAP flexibility. Consequently, appraisers who lack the required knowledge, experience, and access to appropriate data must not be utilized.

Source: *Selling Guide: Fannie Mae Single Family* (Washington, D.C.: Fannie Mae, January 17, 2013), 518. The most current version of the *Selling Guide* can be found at www.fanniemae.com/singlefamily/originating-underwriting.

2014-2015 edition of USPAP clearly states that the appraiser must perform competently when completing the assignment. In contrast, compliance with the GSE and FHA requirement means that an appraiser should not accept an assignment unless and until he or she has attained the necessary level of competency.

It seems a little late to judge competency by the time the written appraisal report has been submitted. An appraiser's competency should be based on his or her qualifications, knowledge of the market area, experience, and completion of continuing education programs. Appraisers should keep copies of their qualifications that detail their professional experience and training. Exhibit 3.2 provides a brief overview of the USPAP competency requirements as compared to those of the GSEs, the US Department of Veterans Affairs (VA), and the FHA/US Department of Housing and Urban Development (HUD).

State Appraiser Boards

The state appraiser boards set the standard in the 1990s when all states instituted state licensing and certification for real estate appraisers, which was one outcome of the Financial Institutions Reform, Recovery and Enforcement Act (FIRREA) of 1989. A minimum number of prescribed qualifying classroom hours were required for appraisers prior to applying for and taking the state licensing exam. Does this imply that a minimum number of qualifying green valuation education hours should also be required? The GSEs have not set a minimum number of hours or type of qualifying green valuation education. Each lender must

	USPAP	GSE	VA	FHA
Exhibit 3.2	**Comparison of Industry Competency Guidelines**			
What Guidelines Govern	Minimum guidelines for all appraisers	Conventional appraisals selling on secondary market	VA loans	FHA loans also referenced as HUD
Guidelines for Accepting Assignments	Requires the appraiser to be competent to perform the assignment, acquire the necessary competency to perform the assignment, or withdraw from the assignment. The appraiser must perform competently when completing the assignment.	The appraiser must have requisite knowledge of the property type prior to accepting the assignment.	The appraiser must have geographical competency and hold a certified residential or general license.	The appraiser must be competent at the time of accepting the assignment (a long-standing HUD policy).

Source: *Uniform Standards of Professional Appraisal Practice*, 2014-2015 ed. (Washington, D.C.: The Appraisal Foundation, 2013), U-vi; US Department of Veterans Affairs, *Lenders Handbook: VA Pamphlet 26-7*, www.benefits.va.gov/warms/pam26_7.asp/; *FHA Single Family Housing Policy Handbook*, Section 1(C)(e)(i)(ii). See Chapters 10-15 of the VA *Lenders Handbook* for specific appraisal-related details.

make that decision, and lenders are held responsible for their choices by the GSEs that purchase the loans. Unfortunately, the lenders are only held responsible for their choice of appraiser at the time of foreclosure, when the loan may be documented with a less-than-credible appraisal.

Court Testimony

One of the first questions an attorney usually asks an appraiser who is testifying as an expert witness is about the appraiser's educational background in the specific property type that qualifies him or her as an "expert." It seems that the courts also view education as the first step in competency. The second step is experience, followed by continued study and research. Green building technology is changing rapidly as research reveals better materials and techniques. A one-hour webinar on green building would not serve as sufficient education in this property type. Continued study with the help of reading materials published by recognized educational organizations will assist appraisers in acquiring knowledge of new techniques and market studies on the topic. The Appraisal Institute offers a professional development program on the valuation of sustainable buildings (www.appraisalinstitute.org/education/green_offerings.aspx). New courses and seminars are continually being added to this program because the Appraisal Institute recognizes that continually updating educational offerings is critical for competency in a rapidly changing market segment.

Lenders and Appraisal Management Companies

A number of lenders and appraisal management companies (AMCs) use questionnaires or applications to qualify appraisers for their vendor lists. Many require appraisers to submit three samples of their work for review as a prerequisite for acceptance. Once an appraiser is on the "rotation" list, he or she is often assumed to be qualified for residential work. The secondary market holds lenders responsible for making choices concerning the competency of the appraiser and the quality of the appraisal products they accept. Appraisers on the rotation list bear a responsibility to turn down assignments that they do not have the competency to handle.

If the applications or questionnaires of lenders and AMCs do not ask for green experience or course work, it is difficult to understand how they measure competency prior to ordering the report. Do they call the appraisers on the list prior to placing the order? In an interview with a representative of one AMC, I was told that they call every appraiser before placing an order on any property to ensure that the appraiser has competency in the specific property type and geographical area.

Prior to placing an appraiser on the rotation list, the lender or AMC is supposed to review the licensing as well as the educational and experience background of the appraiser. However, this takes a "one size fits all" approach to determining appraiser qualifications. One appraiser cannot possibly be an expert or qualified in every property type; it is not humanly possible.

Appraisal Port by FNC, Inc., runs regular online poll questions for appraiser responses. On July 29, 2013, the following question was listed:

> Do any of your clients ever inquire if you have had training, or specialize in, green valuation issues?

This poll ran for one week, and 5,743 appraisers responded. The results indicate that most AMCs do not qualify appraisers prior to placing orders: 0.8% of participants answered "often," 12.5% answered "rarely," and 86.6% answered "never." The reality of the situation is that appraisers have the obligation to reject orders for property types that do not fall into their competency skill set or that are outside their geographical areas of competency.

New Guidance from The Appraisal Foundation

Supplementing the longstanding guidance on competency in USPAP, The Appraisal Foundation has recently addressed competency in green building valuation more directly through the Appraisal Practices Board (APB). In their first exposure draft of the *Valuation of Green Buildings* advisory issued in July 2013, the green/energy efficiency education section states the following:

> Appraisers should endeavor to incorporate green building and energy efficiency into their education regimen. Paths to competency include, but are not limited to, coursework and self-study, as well as attendance at professional seminars and presentations (live and online), offered both by appraisal organizations, as well as organizations like the US Green Building Council (USGBC) and others that specialize in green building and energy efficiency.[2]

---

2. *Valuation of Green Buildings: Background and Core Competency–First Exposure Draft* (Washington, D.C.: The Appraisal Foundation, 2013), 5.

In 2013, a bank sent a survey to appraisers on their vendor list. The survey asked questions similar to the following:

· How many energy-efficient homes with HERS Index ratings have you appraised in the past two years?

· Were the homes new or existing?

· Did you complete the Appraisal Institute's Residential Green and Energy Efficient Addendum as part of the appraisal?

· What challenges did you find in preparing the appraisal?

· Were there sufficient energy-efficient comparables in the neighborhood or market area to complete your appraisal?

· Did you have difficulty in supporting the sale price?

· Did you make an adjustment for energy efficiency? What methods were used for developing the adjustment?

· Please list any special training you have in high-performance (energy-efficient or green) houses.

· Did you complete the Valuation of Sustainable Buildings professional development program sponsored by the Appraisal Institute? If so, please provide copies of certificates for the classes completed.

· How much additional time is needed over the appraisal of a code-built house to provide a credible appraisal report for a green home?

By performing this extra step to ensure competency, the bank exhibited due diligence in qualifying the competency of appraisers for energy-efficient home appraisals. Borrowers seeking loans on energy-efficient homes should seek lenders with due diligence in place for all aspects of the loan process.

The section of the document that covers the topic of thresholds of competence indicates that an appraiser's competency for a particular assignment may be determined based on the appraiser's ability to accurately perform the following tasks:

• Identify the characteristics of the subject property that would cause it to be classified as green or energy-efficient

• Verify these characteristics (with an emphasis on third-party verification)

• Analyze the market to determine if these characteristics contribute to market value

• Develop and report an opinion of the market value of the subject property[3]

This discussion from the APB seems to imply that the appraiser's competence cannot be determined until the report has been reviewed. This also assumes that the person reviewing the report knows enough about high-performance properties to judge the credibility of the report. At this point, the borrower is paying for an appraisal that may or may not be credible. The point of review does not seem like a reasonable occasion to judge competency. Competency conclusions from these different sectors overwhelmingly suggest that competency should be obtained prior to accepting or completing the assignment.

---

3.   Ibid., 23-24.

How the Market Currently Deals with Competency and Complexity in Green Valuation

In the context of professional appraisal standards, the typical valuation of a green building qualifies as a complex appraisal assignment because it most likely involves limited market data and requires the appraiser to have special knowledge and experience. The term *complex appraisal assignment* implies a property type for which little or no market data may be available or that has unusual characteristics requiring the appraiser to have special knowledge and experience to produce a credible assignment result. In other words, a complex assignment involves more time, requires special skills, and should command an appropriate fee.

However, the fees paid for appraisals of green properties often do not correspond with the amount of time required to competently complete these assignments. For example, I recently interviewed Robert C. Oglesby of Appraisal Tek in Arizona, and he indicated that green appraisals take much longer because the lender clients are not current on the topic and more time is spent on conversation and explanation. The additional time spent developing the appraisal opinion and writing the report results in a fee that is only 5% to 10% more than the fee for conventional properties. These typical fees do not seem to be commensurate with the amount of time and skill required to complete the assignment.

Unfortunately, the real estate industry seems to be approaching the green valuation problem as if its practitioners had never experienced new valuation problems before. The appraiser's toolbox contains more than one valuation tool. (The relevant tools for the valuation of green buildings will be discussed in more detail in the next chapter.) Some toolboxes have rusty tools that require sharpening to solve today's valuation issues. For more than 30 years, the Appraisal Institute has taught valuation methods such as paired data analysis, gross rent multiplier times rent or income, depreciated cost analysis, market participant surveys, discounted cash flow analysis, and impact studies as tools for developing value. When did the profession remove all of these tools except for the paired sales method?

More broadly, when did the nonappraiser—such as the underwriter or ordering department—gain the power to dictate the value, the valuation method used, and the development of the report? The answer to this question is, sadly, when appraisers let them do so. The appraiser is clearly responsible for developing and writing a credible report that appropriately addresses the physical, economic, legal, and locational factors of a property. Following poor advice from nonappraisers can lead to reports that are misleading and not credible. It is not likely that the underwriter or client will appear before the state appraiser board when the appraiser is charged with improper appraisal methods.

A market that has little or no sales data on high-performance housing brings out the best in an experienced appraiser, leading him or her to use more than one tool or method to prepare a credible report. Using only one method is not enough in a complex appraisal assignment. A second or third method is necessary as a test of reasonableness. In the case of a new product on the market, it is logical that cost is an excellent test of reasonableness as a secondary method. Cost will most likely set the upper limit of value for the feature, and employing other methods along with cost is prudent appraisal practice.

Developing a credible green appraisal report is a time-consuming task because of the additional effort needed to educate the client about the high-performance characteristics and to collect the necessary documents to provide a credible appraisal. This complex appraisal problem requires an appraiser with the willingness to educate the client on the needed documents, the tenacity to insist that the documents be provided, and the tools to prove adjustments (or lack of adjustments) when high-performance comparables do not exist. Simply gathering the documentation for high-performance properties can take extra days. Appraising green property can add weeks to research and documentation, especially when it comes to proposed construction. Builders or architects may not understand why appraisers need certain documents, and additional conversations may be required to communicate the importance of providing them. It may take several conversations to fully explain how the documents assist in the valuation process. However, once builders understand what the documents mean to the valuation process, they are usually eager to provide the appropriate preliminary ratings on proposed construction. In addition, more builders are completing the Appraisal Institute's Residential Green and Energy Efficient Addendum and providing it to buyers, lenders, agents, and appraisers. This addendum provides a standardization of the green fields and an organized list for documenting the features. (The process of filling out the form will be discussed in Chapter 6.) Appraisers cannot appropriately value what they cannot identify or describe.

In a market without data on green property sales, appraisers should counsel borrowers to seek lenders who understand high-performance valuation and the local market. If a borrower knows that a lender or underwriter will not accept adjustments for high-performance features without relevant sales data (e.g., actual high-performance sales or paired sales), the borrower has the option of finding a lender who will accept other credible methods. Credit unions and small community banks are more receptive to these property types because they often keep their mortgages in-house. When lenders keep their mortgages in-house, they do not always require that the appraisal report meet Fannie Mae or Freddie Mac guidelines. They may be more accepting of supported adjustments for energy efficiency and comparable properties that are beyond a one-mile radius and more than one year from the date of sale of the subject property.

Appraisers report that underwriters often claim that the secondary market does not allow for adjustments without paired sales.

A review of the secondary market guidelines for Fannie Mae and Freddie Mac and for the FHA and the VA does *not* reveal such a rule. However, the secondary mortgage market does require that appraisers support all adjustments.

Qualifying the lender is as important as qualifying the appraiser in any market. Borrowers are not always aware of the difficulties that occur with lending on green properties. Therefore, sales agents and builders must be diligent in counseling borrowers prior to choosing a lender.

Not all lenders are experts in what is known as an *energy efficient mortgage* (EEM), which credits a home's energy efficiency in the mortgage itself. EEMs give borrowers the opportunity to finance cost-effective, energy-saving measures as part of a single mortgage and stretch debt-to-income qualifying ratios on loans, thereby allowing borrowers to qualify for larger loan amounts and better, more energy-efficient homes.[4] To provide a real-life example of the education that is needed and often lacking, a builder of high-performance homes researched Fannie Mae's website to find a local lender offering energy-efficient mortgages. When the builder called this lender, the loan officer at first indicated that she was not sure that the institution participated in the Fannie Mae program but she was sure that the lender had made similar loans before. The builder took the borrower to this lender and explained that an appraiser who knew something about green or high-performance houses would be needed. The lender indicated that *all* the appraisers on the institution's rotation list were qualified. After the appraisal was submitted, the builder reviewed the appraisal report with the borrower and found no mention of the green features. The energy efficiency of the house was rated as average, and the comparable sales data included only conventional-built houses that were 5 to 15 years old with no adjustments made for quality or energy efficiency. An experienced green appraiser was hired after a long talk with the lender, but not without the borrower paying for two appraisals.

The GSEs hold lenders responsible for qualifying appraisers even if a lender uses an appraisal management company (AMC). The appraiser qualification process is too often limited to determining how fast and at what fee the appraiser can complete the report, or the next person on the rotation list is automatically deemed to be "qualified." It seems that the art of qualifying an appraiser has been lost in the last 15 years to lower-fee, fast-service providers.

Establishing competency before making an appointment with an appraiser is appropriate. The client or the ordering department should ask appraisers what classes on green or energy-efficient buildings they have taken in the past five years. As a test, appraisers may be asked to name the six elements of green building. If the appraiser has not had a significant number of green valuation education hours and does not have a clue about the six elements of green building, that person may not be the right appraiser for the assignment.

---

4. Energy Star, www.energystar.gov/index.cfm?c=mortgages.energy_efficient_mortgages.

The Appraisal Institute has an online registry of designated members who have completed the Valuation of Sustainable Buildings professional development program.[5] The program includes a group of green valuation courses (with exams given at the end of each course) to assist appraisers in understanding and valuing green buildings. Successful completion of a minimum of 14 hours of education plus two one-hour exams is required prior to the designated member's name being added to the green registry. As of March 2013, approximately 5,000 members had taken the green classes. Considering that the national registry of the Appraisal Subcommittee contains more than 100,000 active appraisers in the United States, it would be interesting to know how many of that total have taken a green class from any educational provider.[6]

The Solution Is Not Another License Law or Regulation

It is not in all appraisers' best interests for state licensing boards to require the completion of green valuation education programs every continuing education period. Not all appraisers value houses or even commercial buildings. Appraisers often specialize in particular property types such as steel mills, farms, or coal mines. Requiring these appraisers to take green valuation education may not add to their specialty skill sets.

The Appraisal Foundation requires seven hours of green valuation education for all new appraisers entering the profession beginning in 2015. However, this does not address the problem of current licensed or certified appraisers who do not have the knowledge to handle the high-performance appraisal assignment. If McGraw-Hill Construction's *SmartMarket Report: New and Remodeled Green Homes: Transforming the Residential Marketplace* is correct in the estimate that 29% to 38% of all new construction by 2016 will be of high-performance houses, the likelihood that an appraiser will encounter at least one green property is high.[7] However, will that appraiser recognize that the house is a high-performance building and decline the assignment? It is the responsibility of each appraiser to determine if he or she has the professional competency to complete an assignment. Appraisers who turn down assignments because they do not possess the knowledge of the property type should be highly respected by their clients.

Suggested Steps to Competency

Nondesignated appraisers who take the Appraisal Institute's green courses are provided with proof of completing the classes. AMCs or lenders should require such proof. The two required green courses

---

5.   This registry does not include appraisers who have completed the green professional development program but are not designated by the organization.

6.   Appraisal Subcommittee, Active Appraiser Credentials Summary Report, www.asc.gov/National-Registry/ActiveAppraisers.aspx.

7.   McGraw-Hill Construction, *SmartMarket Report: New and Remodeled Green Homes: Transforming the Residential Marketplace* (Bedford, MA: McGraw-Hill, 2012), 1.

for residential appraisers in the Appraisal Institute's professional development program are *Introduction to Green Building: Principles and Concepts* and *Case Studies in Appraising Green Residential Buildings*, each of which includes a one-hour exam. Appraisers must pass the one-hour exam for each course to be placed on the registry.[8]

Experience in appraising this type of property in a given market is another measure of competency. If green construction is new to your area, your experience may be limited. Ideally, a local appraiser who has had credible education and experience is the best choice. Appraisers without experience can collaborate with experienced appraisers outside the market area to gain experience. However, this would not meet the secondary mortgage market requirement of

---

HOW ONE HOMEBUILDERS ASSOCIATION HANDLES CHOOSING AN APPRAISER

Matt Belcher, the director of the High Performance Building Center at the Midwest Energy Efficiency Research Consortium of the University of Missouri-Columbia, developed the following agreement with a local lender. Belcher began using this agreement with all lenders, whether they were lenders that Belcher usually used or those brought in by the client (borrower). Belcher reported that all lenders approached have accepted this agreement, as it also assists them. The St. Louis Homebuilders Association and other organizations have also promoted the agreement, as it helps promote better practices and more education. "Most builders are hesitant to build to a higher level due to the risk, real or perceived," Belcher says. "If we can demonstrate that a proactive approach to removing one of their major hurdles can be taken, it surely cannot hurt. It seems that lenders also have a better comfort level with the third-party verification or certification."[*]

Using an agreement like the following is one way of combating the "rotation list" method of choosing appraisers. This agreement requires lenders to qualify appraisers as they are charged to do by GSEs. The wording in the agreement is as follows:

> This Home is being built/renovated/updated to nationally recognized standards above prevailing code. It is designed and constructed with unique features and materials and with high-efficiency equipment and in accordance with high-efficiency standards. The Lender shall choose an Appraiser educated and knowledgeable in this type of valuation of these specialized Homes. It is understood that unless said Appraiser can provide verification of education and knowledge, they will not be permitted to conduct the appraisal for this project.

The agreement with the lender should not be necessary because the GSEs already require appraiser competency prior to accepting the assignment. However, the proactive step taken by Mr. Belcher and the homebuilders can make a major difference in the valuation process.

Neither the Dodd-Frank Wall Street Reform and Consumer Protection Act nor the GSEs allow the borrower to choose the appraiser.[†] Appraisers are expected to be competent based on the guidelines that have been in place for several years. However, when the guidelines are not followed, it takes bold steps such as those taken in St. Louis to change the status quo.

Mr. Belcher's language has been enhanced by the National Association of Homebuilders (NAHB) and promoted through their recent blog at www.nahb.org. The language change is as follows:

> This Home is being built/renovated/updated to nationally recognized standards above prevailing code. It is designed and constructed with unique features and materials and with high-efficiency equipment and in accordance with high-efficiency standards. The Lender shall choose an Appraiser educated and knowledgeable in this type of valuation of these specialized Homes, preferably an appraiser who holds a professional appraisal designation that requires advanced education on such issues as the valuation of sustainable buildings (e.g., MAI or SRA designations from the Appraisal Institute). The appraiser shall provide verification of green valuation education of 14 hours or more from a qualified educational provider and knowledge to be permitted to conduct the appraisal for this project.

---

* Matt Belcher (director, High Performance Building Center, Midwest Energy Efficiency Research Consortium, University of Missouri-Columbia), in discussion with the author, March 2013.
† A brief summary of the Dodd-Frank Wall Street Reform and Consumer Protection Act is available at www.banking.senate,gov/public/_files/070110_Dodd_Frank_Wall_Street_Reform_Comprehensive_Summary_Final.pdf.

---

8. Note that Appraisal Institute courses include exams but seminars do not. Some educational providers may only offer green programs that do not include exams.

competency prior to accepting the assignment. Ideally, an appraiser should partner with another competent appraiser to gain knowledge and experience prior to accepting an assignment of his or her own.

Federal Green Mandates Versus the URAR Form

Federal, state, and local government agencies are mandating green building through international, federal, and local building codes. Although the GSEs are government agencies, it appears that they are not on the same page as the federal, state, and local government agencies. A review of the mortgage lending appraisal form developed by the GSEs will explain this situation.

The Uniform Residential Appraisal Report (URAR), also known as Fannie Mae Form 1004 or Freddie Mac Form 70, dated March 2005 (and available online at www.fanniemae.com/content/guide_form/1004.pdf), does not address high-performance features. This results in mixed messages and misuse by appraisers and underwriters lacking competency. Underwriters need a basic knowledge of green building to be able to make appropriate appraisal review decisions. Appraisers and underwriters often rely on checklists on standardized forms to guide them through a process. If the property or its features do not fit in the boxes, appraisers may make errors of omission or commission, as explained in Standards Rule 1-1(b) of USPAP. Omitting pertinent facts regarding a property's physical, locational, and economic attributes may result in inappropriate questions or responses from the underwriter. Underwriters need well-documented reports to make sound decisions regarding a property's eligibility for a loan and the credibility of the data presented.

Appraisers are challenged by USPAP to avoid committing substantial errors of omission or commission that would significantly affect an appraisal. Complying with this standards rule requires diligence in identifying and analyzing the property factors that would have significant effects on the credibility of the assignment results. In appraisals of high-performance properties, appraisers must analyze and identify the physical, economic, and locational features that affect the value conclusions. Omitting the description of the property or the economic attributes that may apply to the property as compared to properties that may not have those benefits could result in an error of omission or commission. Even if an appraiser has analyzed all the features of a high-performance property in the report, the report could still be misleading if it does not address these features or the analysis.

Keeping in mind the six elements of green building, consider how the following form sections illustrate how outdated it is regarding high-performance houses:

- Site
- Improvements
- Sales comparison

- Retired Fannie Mae Energy Addendum
- Scope of work
- Appraiser's certification

According to the previously mentioned McGraw-Hill Construction *SmartMarket Report*, 29% to 38% of all new construction will be high-performance housing by the year 2016. With this in mind, it seems reasonable to assume that existing high-performance housing retrofits will follow. If existing housing is not updated to meet high-performance market expectations, a valuation and marketing storm will occur because the highest and best use may become "as improved with retrofits."

Site and the Site Section of the URAR Form

The site section of the URAR form is shown in Exhibit 3.3. Can you find any green elements, such as orientation, landscaping, water efficiencies, and walk score addressed in this section of the form?

Exhibit 3.3   URAR Site Section

Dimensions		Area	Shape		View		
Specific Zoning Classification			Zoning Description				
Zoning Compliance ☐ Legal ☐ Legal Nonconforming (Grandfathered Use) ☐ No Zoning ☐ Illegal (describe)							
Is the highest and best use of the subject property as improved (or as proposed per plans and specifications) the present use? ☐ Yes ☐ No If No, describe							
Utilities Public Other (describe)		Public Other (describe)			Off-site Improvements—Type	Public	Private
Electricity ☐ ☐		Water ☐ ☐			Street	☐	☐
Gas ☐ ☐		Sanitary Sewer ☐ ☐			Alley	☐	☐
FEMA Special Flood Hazard Area ☐ Yes ☐ No FEMA Flood Zone			FEMA Map #		FEMA Map Date		
Are the utilities and off-site improvements typical for the market area? ☐ Yes ☐ No If No, describe							
Are there any adverse site conditions or external factors (easements, encroachments, environmental conditions, land uses, etc.)? ☐ Yes ☐ No If Yes, describe							

Three lines are available for the appraiser to include green site elements. The appraiser has the option to move the site description to the addendum if these three lines are not sufficient. Using the Appraisal Institute's Residential Green and Energy Efficient Addendum (RGEEA) with this form is one way to handle these missing items. The appraiser could simply write "See attached RGEEA" on the blank lines of the site section.

The site section of the RGEEA is shown in Exhibit 3.4 to illustrate how it complements the site section of the URAR form. Site and water elements of green building are addressed in this section of the RGEEA. The RGEEA also has a large comments section to allow for elaboration on features that are not listed in the checkbox sections.

Energy Efficiency and the Improvements Section of the URAR Form

The section of the URAR designated for description of the improvements is shown in Exhibit 3.5. Things are looking up for energy efficiency because two lines are provided to address special energy-

Exhibit 3.4   RGEEA Site Section

Location - Site		
The following items are considered within the appraised value of the subject property:		

Walk Score	Score:	Source: (Example: http://www.walkscore.com)		
Public Transportation	☐ Bus – Distance: Blocks	☐ Train – Distance: Blocks	☐ Subway – Distance: Blocks
Site	Orientation - front faces: ☐ East/West ☐ North/South	Landscaping: ☐ Water Efficient ☐ Natural	
Comments		

Exhibit 3.5   URAR Improvements Section

General Description	Foundation	Exterior Description	materials/condition	Interior	materials/condition
Units ☐ One ☐ One with Accessory Unit	☐ Concrete Slab ☐ Crawl Space	Foundation Walls		Floors	
# of Stories	☐ Full Basement ☐ Partial Basement	Exterior Walls		Walls	
Type ☐ Det. ☐ Att. ☐ S-Det./End Unit	Basement Area sq. ft.	Roof Surface		Trim/Finish	
☐ Existing ☐ Proposed ☐ Under Const.	Basement Finish %	Gutters & Downspouts		Bath Floor	
Design (Style)	☐ Outside Entry/Exit ☐ Sump Pump	Window Type		Bath Wainscot	
Year Built	Evidence of ☐ Infestation	Storm Sash/Insulated		Car Storage ☐ None	
Effective Age (Yrs)	☐ Dampness ☐ Settlement	Screens		☐ Driveway # of Cars	
Attic ☐ None	Heating ☐ FWA ☐ HWBB ☐ Radiant	Amenities ☐ Woodstove(s) #		Driveway Surface	
☐ Drop Stair ☐ Stairs	☐ Other Fuel	☐ Fireplace(s) # ☐ Fence		☐ Garage # of Cars	
☐ Floor ☐ Scuttle	Cooling ☐ Central Air Conditioning	☐ Patio/Deck ☐ Porch		☐ Carport # of Cars	
☐ Finished ☐ Heated	☐ Individual ☐ Other	☐ Pool ☐ Other		☐ Att. ☐ Det. ☐ Built-in	

Appliances ☐Refrigerator ☐Range/Oven ☐Dishwasher ☐Disposal ☐Microwave ☐Washer/Dryer ☐Other (describe)

Finished area **above** grade contains: Rooms   Bedrooms   Bath(s)   Square Feet of Gross Living Area Above Grade

Additional features (special energy efficient items, etc.) ◄

Describe the condition of the property (including needed repairs, deterioration, renovations, remodeling, etc.).

Are there any physical deficiencies or adverse conditions that affect the livability, soundness, or structural integrity of the property? ☐ Yes ☐ No If Yes, describe

Does the property generally conform to the neighborhood (functional utility, style, condition, use, construction, etc.)? ☐ Yes ☐ No If No, describe

efficient items in this section. However, considering the differences between a code-built house and a high-performance house, do you think this section provides enough space for the description of high-performance features? This forces a diligent appraiser to move a narrative description to the textual addendum, where it may or may not be read by the underwriter.

Underwriters and reviewers often overlook narrative descriptions of energy and green features. Considering the high volume of appraisal reports that underwriters must review, it is only logical that a more standardized addendum for these special features would be useful for these readers of appraisal reports.

The last question in this section of the form, which asks if the property conforms to the neighborhood construction, is often poorly answered in cases when high-performance houses are built among houses that are not high-performance. Note that building high-performance homes on in-fill lots is encouraged to promote smart growth using the infrastructure already in place and to avoid urban sprawl. If the property being appraised is one of the first high-performance houses in the area, it may exceed the construction standards of the majority of the houses in the neighborhood. The operating costs of a high-performance house should be lower than those for other conventional-built houses in the neighborhood. Both of these items are worth mentioning, and they build the case for possible adjustments if the only sales available for comparison are of conventional-built homes.

The Sales Comparison Section of the URAR Form

The sales comparison section of the URAR form shown in Exhibit 3.6 provides a line for energy-efficient items and three blank lines for additional features that are not itemized. This section provides adequate space to develop value if appropriate descriptions and sales are applied. The previous site and improvements sections set the stage for this section of the report. If the subject property is described appropriately, the sales search parameters are more easily defined, resulting in substitute properties or properties with similar characteristics that compete for the same buyer type. The problem lies in the subject property being described appropriately. Using the URAR without additional text addenda or the RGEEA does not provide underwriters an adequate foundation for understanding high-performance property characteristics. The use of the URAR alone usually results in the builder, agent, or owner of the high-performance property asking how the appraiser considered the features of the high-performance house if those features were not identified in the report.

In Exhibit 3.6, the arrows point to the areas where energy-efficient and high-performance features can be analyzed. To add insult to injury, the Uniform Appraisal Dataset (UAD) currently used by Fannie Mae and Freddie Mac was developed to standardize some 60 fields on the URAR, but none of the required UAD fields addresses

Exhibit 3.6   URAR Sales Comparison Section

FEATURE	SUBJECT	COMPARABLE SALE # 1		COMPARABLE SALE # 2		COMPARABLE SALE # 3	
Address							
Proximity to Subject							
Sale Price	$		$		$		$
Sale Price/Gross Liv. Area	$ sq. ft.	$ sq. ft.		$ sq. ft.		$ sq. ft.	
Data Source(s)							
Verification Source(s)							
VALUE ADJUSTMENTS	DESCRIPTION	DESCRIPTION	+(-) $ Adjustment	DESCRIPTION	+(-) $ Adjustment	DESCRIPTION	+(-) $ Adjustment
Sale or Financing Concessions							
Date of Sale/Time							
Location							
Leasehold/Fee Simple							
Site							
View							
Design (Style)							
Quality of Construction							
Actual Age							
Condition							
Above Grade Room Count	Total Bdrms. Baths	Total Bdrms. Baths		Total Bdrms. Baths		Total Bdrms. Baths	
Gross Living Area	sq. ft.	sq. ft.		sq. ft.		sq. ft.	
Basement & Finished Rooms Below Grade							
Functional Utility							
Heating/Cooling							
Energy Efficient Items	←						
Garage/Carport							
Porch/Patio/Deck							
	←						
Net Adjustment (Total)		☐ + ☐ -	$	☐ + ☐ -	$	☐ + ☐ -	$
Adjusted Sale Price of Comparables		Net Adj. % Gross Adj. %	$	Net Adj. % Gross Adj. %	$	Net Adj. % Gross Adj. %	$

(left margin label: SALES COMPARISON APPROACH)

green features or energy efficiency. This makes it difficult for the GSEs to track mortgages of green houses.

Energy Addendum

In 1989, Fannie Mae and Freddie Mac promoted the income capitalization approach for energy efficiency, but their Energy Addendum (Fannie Mae Form 1004A/Freddie Mac Form 70A, dated June 1989) was later retired. This addendum included a number of energy features and a mathematical formula for developing the value of energy savings using a present value calculation of the energy saved. The form also indicated that this method could be used in the absence of market data, which is further evidence that paired data analysis is not the only method that has ever been taught or used. Exhibit 3.7 shows the portion of the retired form with the application of the income capitalization approach suggested for estimating the contributory value of energy savings.

The arrow in Exhibit 3.7 points to a test of reasonableness via applying the cost approach to estimate the total cost of the installed items less depreciation. The instructions indicate that the lesser of either the present worth of the estimated savings or the installed cost

Part 2 - Estimate of value of energy-efficient items

This section can be used to help estimate the value of energy-efficient items only when adequate comparable market data are not available.

In such cases, the value of the energy-efficient items should be the lesser of

(a) the present worth of the estimated savings in utility costs, as determined by capitalizing the savings at an interest rate that is not less than the current interest rate for home mortgages for a period that does not exceed the lesser of the item's expected physical life or seven years, or

(b) the installed cost of the energy-efficient item or construction technique, less any physical, functional, and external depreciation.   ⬅

For example, if the subject property is an existing house with inadequate insulation and infiltration barriers - such as one without storm windows, caulking and weatherstripping - and the estimated savings per month is $35 for upgrading the property (based on an energy audit/rating), the appraiser could use the following calculations as a guide.

Installed cost (less depreciation)	$2,500	
Expected life	7 + years	
Expected monthly savings	$35 per month	$420 x 4.789 = $2,011.38
Expected annual savings	$420 per year	
Present value factor (annual compound interest at 10.5% for 7 years)	$4.789	

For this example, it would appear reasonable (**only if adequate comparable data were not available**) that a typical purchaser might pay a premium of $2,000 for the property as improved with the suggested energy-related items.

---

of the energy-efficient item or technique less depreciation should be used. However, the appraiser should decide which indication has the most strength and then reconcile accordingly.

The income capitalization approach requires support for the inputs of expected life, energy monthly savings, and annual compound interest rate used. This invites the obvious question about why the income capitalization approach is not valid today. If Fannie Mae and Freddie Mac provided appraisers with this fill-in-the-blank form for use in the 1980s, why are some underwriters indicating that the income capitalization approach cannot be used to support an adjustment for energy-efficient items in a market with limited sales data? A simple letter from Fannie Mae or Freddie Mac to clarify that the income capitalization approach is acceptable if appropriately supported would solve many problems in today's market.

The first exposure draft of The Appraisal Foundation's *Valuation of Green Buildings: Background and Core Competency* advisory specifically indicates that the appraiser is expected to conduct adequate market research to support the use of gross rent multipliers (GRMs), discounted cash flow analysis, or similar income-based valuation techniques.

Case Study: Passive House

Consider the following case study of present value developed with no support for a home built to the Passivhaus, or "Passive House," standard, in which thermal comfort is achieved by post-heating or post-cooling of the fresh air mass to provide sufficient indoor air quality conditions without additional air recirculation.[9] An appraisal of a Passivhaus-constructed home had an across-the-board adjustment for energy-efficient features. The lump-sum dollar adjustment was based on the present value of the energy savings. Dividing the lump-sum adjustment by the

---

9.   Passivhaus Institut, www.passivhaus.org.uk/standard.jsp?id=122.

sales prices of the comparable properties resulted in a 5% to 9% line-item adjustment. A line-item adjustment will raise a red flag if it exceeds 10% unless the appraiser has documented good support for it. In this case, the appraiser provided the following adequate support:

> The subject is to be constructed using Passivhaus construction methods and techniques, offering significant energy savings to the dwelling over its economic life. The builder estimates a monthly energy savings of $559.97. This estimate projects energy inflation of 2% over a 30-year period. The present value of the contributory value of the monthly energy savings of $559.97 is calculated with an annual interest rate of 6% for a 70-year period, resulting in a present value of $110,296, rounded to $110,000.

The calculation can be developed using an HP-12C financial calculator. The inputs used by the appraiser were as follows:

6% interest rate	6 g i	0.50
70 years	70 g n	840.00
$559.97	559.97 CHS PMT	-559.97
	PV	– $110,296.92

Underwriters may have concerns about the application of the gross rent multiplier in calculating an adjustment, and they may ask questions such as the following:

1. The comments indicate an energy inflation rate of 2% over a 30-year period.
    - What is the source for the 2% inflation rate?
    - Why use 30 years when the present value calculation is over 70 years?
    - Why is this information provided when it was not considered in the present value calculation? Is it relevant to the value conclusion?

2. What is the energy savings provided by the builder based on?
    - Does the appraiser have sufficient confidence in the data provided by others, as per USPAP?[10]
    - Was a HERS Index preliminary report provided to support the $559.97 in monthly savings? If the subject property is proposed construction but based on specifications and blueprints, the HERS rater can provide a HERS Index rating that is specifically watermarked as *preliminary*. The appraiser should make the appraisal subject to the final HERS Index report as indicated in the preliminary report.
    - Did the appraiser simply take the owner, agent, or builder's word for an energy savings? If so, this will usually raise questions as to the credibility of the data.

---

10. *Uniform Standards of Professional Appraisal Practice*, 2014-2015 ed. (Washington D.C.: The Appraisal Foundation, 2013), U-27.

3. What is the basis for the 6% interest rate?
   - USPAP requires support for the rate applied.
   - Simply stating a rate is not sufficient. Would the typical buyer consider the 30-year residential mortgage rate or other alternative investment rates?
4. Why was 70 years used for the discounting period?
   - Support for this useful life estimate should be provided. The Energy Addendum used the expected or useful life of the energy features. The Marshall & Swift/Boeckh *Residential Cost Handbook* provides support, as would manufacturer's estimates, home inspector reports, studies by various building trade organizations, and a variety of other sources.

Scope of Work

Every appraisal report is required to at least summarize the scope of work of the appraisal assignment. The appraiser can address the steps taken to develop the appraisal in this part of the report. The resources researched and individuals interviewed in the process are usually discussed in this section. The appraiser can also discuss steps or approaches that were omitted and explain why they were left out.

The URAR form has a standard limiting condition section with a standard scope of work statement, shown below. Note that this statement clearly does not address the concerns of a complex appraisal problem, such as a high-performance property.

> The scope of work for this appraisal is defined by the complexity of this appraisal assignment and the reporting requirements of this appraisal report form, including the following definition of market value, statement of assumptions and limiting conditions, and certifications. The appraiser must, at a minimum: (1) perform a complete visual inspection of the interior and exterior areas of the subject property, (2) inspect the neighborhood, (3) inspect each of the comparable sales from at least the street, (4) research, verify, and analyze data from reliable public and/or private sources, and (5) report his or her analysis, opinions, and conclusions in this appraisal report.

This wording is generic and could not possibly address every property type. The following examples provide some additional language that might be necessary to include in reports for appraisals of high-performance properties:

- "The HERS Index report provided by the builder has been reviewed in its entirety and is the basis for the estimated average annual utility costs and energy ratings."
- "The green rating and worksheet provided by the builder are included in this report and are relied upon for detailing green features."
- "The green features identified in the comparable sales were from the MLS and were verified with agents involved in the transaction."
- "The AI Residential Green and Energy Efficient Addendum was completed by the third-party HERS Rater and reviewed by me.

The data is adequate based on a visual inspection and the supporting documents provided. However, I am not an expert in building science technology."

This language may require editing for specific appraisal problems. It is in no way meant to be a standard blurb for every appraisal. If an appraiser finds errors or areas of concern in the documents provided, those issues should be clearly identified in the appraisal report.

Appraiser's Certification

The URAR form includes a standard certification statement that must be signed by the appraiser. Item 11 in the certification requires the appraiser to certify his or her knowledge and experience in the property type:

> 11. I have knowledge and experience in appraising this type of property in this market area.

Signing this certification could be problematic for an appraiser who does not have competency in the specific property type.

The Energy Report

The Fannie Mae Energy Report provides additional evidence that the income capitalization approach has been used in valuations of owner-occupied residential properties for many years. The income capitalization approach is used to develop the value of energy-efficient features and applied in the sales comparison approach.

Like the previously discussed Energy Addendum, the Fannie Mae Energy Report was also used in the 1980s to value energy-efficient features. The Energy Report is no longer used, but it can still be provided by third-party Home Energy Rating System (HERS) certifiers who use energy modeling software. REM/*Rate* is an energy modeling software program that provides a present value or valuation contribution for energy savings. This would be an application of the income capitalization approach to value that some underwriters are currently insisting cannot be used on residential owner-occupied properties.

When the Fannie Mae Energy Report was used, the underwriter had the option of adding the indicated value to the appraised value if the appraiser did not attribute value for energy efficiency. The use of this form in the past dismisses those who say that the income capitalization approach cannot be used on residential properties or cannot be combined with the sales comparison approach. For complex appraisal assignments, it is important to consider all the tools in the appraiser's toolbox to arrive at a credible value opinion. Applying tests of reasonableness adds strength to the concluded opinion. The previous excerpt from the Energy Addendum shown in Exhibit 3.7 shows the steps involved in estimating energy savings.

The income capitalization method of estimating energy savings is similar to the methods taught today in Appraisal Institute courses. However, some appraisers have told me that using this method resulted in strong opposition from underwriters.

A Review of the Appraiser's Toolbox

Appraisers have a variety of tools or methods that provide reliable value indications. However, the data is not always perfect because market participants may make buying decisions that are not always logical. When a large amount of data is available, value trends can be more easily developed using a variety of methods. However, each valuation method should be tested for reasonableness by comparing its results with those obtained from other methods.

The market determines value, while appraisers develop value opinions based on market data using the following methods, which will be discussed in this chapter:

- Cost analysis
- Use of a gross rent multiplier
- Discounted cash flow analysis
- Paired data analysis

Appraisers must have sufficient knowledge of the property's type and features in order to understand what kind of data is needed to develop an opinion of value. This is a major consideration in complex appraisal assignments.

The Appraisal Port website (www.appraisalport.com) by software technology company FNC Inc. presented a poll question in July 2013 asking visitors how much a 5-kilowatt-hour solar photovoltaic (PV) system would add to value. Some 5,099 respondents replied, with more than 28% indicating that such a system has no value. More than 45% indicated that they were not sure what the value contribution would be. The remaining respondents either indicated that the value fell somewhere within a range starting at $1,000 and going up to as high as over $20,000 or stated that the value depended on the type of system used. Those who responded that they were not sure answered correctly because the question didn't provide enough information about the solar PV system for an appraiser to render a credible value opinion of it. Answers to the following questions would first be required in order to provide a credible value opinion of the system:

- How old is the system?

- How much energy does it produce?
- In what part of the country is the property located? (Properties in higher altitudes are closer to the sun and usually produce more energy.)
- How long is the warranty term?
- What is the *azimuth*, or direction that the solar system faces?
- Do the panels have shading?
- Has the inverter been replaced? When?
- How prevalent are solar PV systems in this market?
- What is the kilowatt cost in this location?

Sound appraisal practice prescribes that appraisers have support for their values. However, zero can be a value and requires as much support as a concrete monetary value. Poll participants who answered that the PV system was worth $0 to $20,000 provided a value without having knowledge of the system. Therefore, they would not be adhering to sound appraisal practices if they were providing such a value indication for an appraisal assignment.

Cost Analysis

Cost analysis is the easiest method for buyers and sellers to research and is often the basis for buyers' and sellers' decisions. Cost does not equal value, but when consumers know an item's cost, that information affects the determination of the item's value and usually sets the upper limit of value. When a new building product arrives on the market, buyers make purchasing decisions based on its cost and perceived value. Some lenders or underwrithers may argue that the cost approach is not a basis for supporting adjustments in the sales comparison approach. If this is your belief, consider how buyers make their decisions. It is the appraiser's job to base the analysis of cost on the typical reactions of buyers and sellers in the market.

The cost approach is applied based on the cost of the feature or property as of the effective date of value, which is typically the date of the site visit for lending purposes. Appraisers have different sources for estimating costs; these sources may include national cost services, local builders or contractors, or new construction sales.

Depreciation comes in a variety of forms such as physical wear and tear, functional obsolescence, or external obsolescence. The difference between the cost of an item today and the amount the market is willing to pay is the depreciation amount.

The Fannie Mae/Freddie Mac Energy Addendum form discussed in Chapter 3 of this book suggests using the cost approach less depreciation as a secondary method to the present worth or discounted cash flow method. The logic behind using the cost approach to support adjustments is simple. An item's contributory value is equal to the cost less depreciation from all causes. In other words, items or features are worth their cost less any depreciation that the market indicates is applicable. Market participants may not use the term *depreciation*, but they do apply the concept. Even a new product can have depreciation if market participants perceive its value as less than its cost.

For example, the functional obsolescence charged in Exhibit 4.1 is for a superadequacy. The market is not willing to pay the full cost of a 4-kilowatt solar PV array. Therefore, the difference between what buyers are willing to pay and the cost is charged to obsolescence. Paired data analysis of a house sold with a solar PV system and a similar house without a solar PV system provided the $4,800 functional obsolescence charged. When incentives are available, they often offset the obsolescence.

Exhibit 4.1	Depreciated Cost Supporting the Contributory Value of a 4-Kilowatt Solar PV Array
Cost Less Depreciation	**Support**
$32,000	Cost based on survey of three local installers
- 8,000	**Physical depreciation** based on the age-life method using an actual age of 5 years / 20 useful life based on warranty term, or 25% × $32,000
- 4,800	**Functional obsolescence** based on the discounted value of the energy produced. An additional -15% is applied based on paired data analysis, or $32,000 × -0.15
– $12,800	
$19,200, or $4,800 per kilowatt estimated value based on cost	

STRENGTHS AND WEAKNESSES OF DEPRECIATED COST ANALYSIS

Strengths:

- Cost analysis is usually the easiest and least time-consuming procedure for residential appraisers to use. It is most applicable in new construction and complex properties. It provides good support for individual features that are new to the market.
- Cost data is easy to support through national cost services or local sources.
- Cost represents the actions of buyers in purchasing decisions.
- Cost is logical in most cases.
- The 1989 Fannie Mae/Freddie Mac Energy Addendum form supports cost analysis as a test of reasonableness.

Weaknesses:

- A new product may not have cost in the market, resulting in difficulty in measuring all forms of loss (depreciation) in the early marketing stage. Even a new feature could have depreciation in the form of a superadequacy, indicating that the market is not willing to pay the cost.
- Costs of newer green materials and technology may not be readily available through normal sources. This weakness is minor because of the growth of high-performance features in the market.

Reasons an Underwriter Might Reject This Method:

- Cost or depreciation does not have documented support because the basis for cost and depreciation figures is not provided.
- A secondary method is not presented to provide a test of reasonableness.

The ratio of actual age to physical life (based on the warranty term) is the easiest step in supporting physical depreciation only. The solar PV system may have additional loss, known as a *superadequacy* (the result of cost that will not be recognized in the market), or functional obsolescence. If an appraiser does not have paired sales or another method to support the estimate of obsolescence, this cost method becomes less reliable. If the client does not accept the DCF method and an appraiser uses it as support for the superadequacy adjustment in the depreciated cost method, both methods will be rejected.

It has been my experience that the rejection of proven methodology is usually the result of failing to provide adequate support for the method. Appraisers who take the time to explain and support the method with factual data receive positive responses. Showing the math is not enough. Appraisers need to provide the details behind the math as well.

Supporting this method requires cost and market data. Cost data is easy to support, but the market data may be impossible to find if the local MLS does not have appropriate data fields. If you do not have specifics on the solar PV system, such as the capacity in kilowatts, it is impossible to value the feature using any method.

Market Extraction of Current Construction Cost

New construction sales can offer good data on direct costs extracted from the market. If the site value and site improvements can be deducted from the sale price, the remainder is the amount attributed to the cost of the structure. A good example of cost extracted from a sale of a certified green property compared to a similar code-built property is shown in Exhibit 4.2.

Exhibit 4.2	Cost Comparisons			
	High-Performance Sale A	Sale Price	Code-Built Sale B	Sale Price
Sale date	5/20XX		4/20XX	
Sale price		$185,000		$177,000
$/sq. ft. living area	$103		$98	
Seller concessions	0		0	
Lot size (sq. ft.)	12,500	-$33,000	13,900	-$33,000
Style	Ranch		Ranch	
Quality	Good		Good	
Age	New		New	
Living area (sq. ft.)	1,800		1,812	
Bedrooms	3		3	
Baths	2.5		2.5	
Porches	Entry/screened		Entry/screened	
Site improvements	Landscaping/irrigation	-$9,000	Landscaping/irrigation	-$7,000
Net cost of improvements		$143,000		$137,000
New cost $/sq. ft. living area		$79.44		$75.61

The example in Exhibit 4.2 is for educational purposes only and is not an actual set of sales. This comparison illustrates how an appraiser can extract cost from the market for both a high-performance house and a code-built house. The appraiser must have support for the value of the lot and cost of site improvements to develop the net cost of the improvements.

In the illustration, the additional cost of 5% to build the high-performance house is attributed to all features of high performance. The illustration falls within the range of the 5% to 7% cost suggested by the McGraw-Hill Construction 2012 *SmartMarket Report*.[1]

This type of data is invaluable on a local basis. An appraiser who can continually track this type of cost data directly from market sales will have excellent evidence as support for the cost approach. This type of data will become more accessible as databases improve to allow such sales to be identified with sufficient details to do a credible comparison.

Gross Rent Multipliers

The monthly energy savings of a high-performance home can be converted into a contributory value or adjustment by using gross rent multiplier analysis. The gross rent multiplier (*GRM*) is a relationship between monthly rent and market value (sale price of property ÷ monthly rent at time of sale = *GRM*). Property owners or buyers anticipate a monthly energy savings or additional income that will stay in their pockets, as shown in Exhibit 4.3.

Developing the contributory value of energy savings with the *GRM* utilizes the same concept that is used for estimating the value of a garage. For example, if the garage will bring an additional $100 in rent monthly and the market indicates that a *GRM* of 110 is appropriate for this property type, then the product of the additional rent

---

Exhibit 4.3 Example of the Contributory Value of Energy Savings Using the *GRM*

Description	Upgrades: Low-E Windows, Energy-Efficient HVAC, R-41 Insulation*	Support
Monthly energy savings	$100	Energy savings based on last 12 months of utility bills compared to the average utility bill of similarly sized houses with similar occupants in the neighborhood.
GRM	110	Sale of 406 Easy St. at $121,000/$1,100 rent per month at time of sale. Sale is in the same neighborhood as the subject.

Indicated value of energy savings: $100 × 110 = $11,000

Test of reasonableness based on depreciated cost of upgrades: $18,000

* The R-value is the insulation rating that reflects the ability of the insulation to resist the flow of heat.

---

1. McGraw-Hill Construction, *SmartMarket Report: New and Remodeled Green Homes: Transforming the Residential Marketplace* (Bedford, MA: McGraw-Hill, 2012).

and the *GRM*, $100 × 110, indicates a value for the garage at $11,000. The appraiser must use a secondary method for a test of reasonableness. Is the *GRM* indication for a garage more than the cost? Does the *GRM* reflect paired sales indications for a garage? If the answer to the first question is yes or the answer to the second question is no, the *GRM* method should not be used because the estimate it would yield would fall outside the range of what is considered reasonable.

Estimating monthly energy savings can be done in the following ways:

- Proposed construction should have a preliminary HERS Index that should provide not only the index rating but also the estimated energy savings. Review the energy tracking section of this text for a better understanding of the report.

- For existing housing, comparing the energy usage to the comparables' energy usage or to neighborhood housing of similar sizes and ages should provide a reasonable estimate of savings.[2] The owner will need to provide utility bills for the last 12 months in order for the appraiser to be able to develop the annual or average monthly energy costs. Use caution when relying on actual bills.

How can you develop a *GRM* without a sale that was rented at the time it sold? The proxy method of developing a *GRM* shown in Exhibit 4.4 compares a house that sold to a similar house rented at or near the time of sale (sale price/gross monthly rent = *GRM*). This method is reliable and has been taught in appraisal classes for many years. It is the method investors use in estimating how much they will pay for a house. Ask a number of investors who purchase residential property for investment purposes how they estimate the price they will pay.

In Exhibit 4.5 later in this chapter, the adjustment indication of $2,100 for energy efficiency should be tested by a secondary method. How does the additional cost of the energy-efficient items compare to this amount? How does it compare to studies or the present value

Exhibit 4.4	Proxy Method for Developing a *GRM*	
Description	**Sale A**	**Rental B**
Sale price/rent	$209,000	$1,900 per month
Date of sale/rental	3/4/XX	2/12/XX (1-yr. lease began)
Gross living area (sq. ft.)	1,700	1,650
Parking	2-car garage attached	2-car garage attached
Room count	7/3.2.1	6/3.2.1
GRM based on Sale A versus Rental B = $209,000/$1,900 = 110 *GRM*		

2. For example, the Madison Gas and Electric Company offers a search-by-address function on their website for average utility costs at www.mge.com/customer-service/home/average-use-cost/index.htm. Other utility companies may offer similar services.

Strengths:

· The *GRM* is easy to develop when data is available.

· It addresses the economic side of residential real estate.

Weaknesses:

· Data is not readily available on some property types, including rural properties or high-end custom homes.

· Buyers of owner-occupied property do not typically use this method. However, it can be applied as secondary support for other methods.

Reasons an Underwriter Might Reject This Method:

· The analysis does not provide support for the *GRM* or energy savings.

· The result is outside the realm of reasonableness, or higher than costs. According to the *SmartMarket Report*, high-performance homes cost on average 5% more than non-green homes by dedicated green builders. So a *GRM* indication that is substantially more than the cost suggests that the *GRM* indication may not be reasonable. Alternatively, it may suggest that the subject property has features that would exceed the average high-performance house. The appraisal should address the possibility of superadequacy if the features of the property appraised cost much more than the typical high-performance property or more than the market will bear.

· The adjustment causes the property's value to fall outside the typical price range of the neighborhood quoted in the neighborhood section of the appraisal report.

---

of the savings? Always consider a test of reasonableness to produce results that are credible, believable, and market oriented.

The *GRM* method should be used with a secondary method and reconciled. Using this method alone will usually raise a question in a neighborhood of owner-occupied homes. Nevertheless, when applied along with another method, the use of *GRM*s adds credibility to the adjustment process and meets USPAP requirements.

Discounted Cash Flow Analysis

The appraisal of a residential property with a solar PV system provides a good example of using discounted cash flow (DCF) analysis in green valuation. Discounting the value of the income stream or the energy produced in today's dollars results in a present value of the energy produced. Some lenders, underwriters, or even government agencies argue that the income capitalization approach is not applicable in residential properties because the house is not rented or because buyers and sellers do not consider the income.

The definition of *market value* considers a well-informed buyer and seller acting in their own best interests. If the buyer understands the function of the solar PV system and the value of the energy produced, he or she is well informed and able to make a reasonable decision. Agents report that some buyers are not willing to pay more for a house with a solar PV system if they do not have knowledge of how the system works (i.e., the financial benefit to the owner). Once these unknowledgeable buyers are provided with reliable information about the system, they are more likely to make the purchase. Marketing plays a major role in educating the public on these kinds of systems. It is crucial to educate appraisers and agents on solar products that are gaining popularity in the market.

Estimating the present value of energy savings for a high-performance house provides another example of DCF in green valuation. Comparing the energy costs of the property to comparable sales energy estimates is the first step in determining if an adjustment is warranted in the sales comparison approach. If the property being appraised has energy costs that are much less than those of competing properties and the energy savings can be attributed to the structure rather than the lifestyle of the occupant, the discounted cash flow could be applied.

Statement 2 of the 2014-2015 edition of USPAP addresses the inputs of the DCF model. It suggests that discount rates and estimates of reversion should be derived from data and information in the real estate and capital markets. Prior to using DCF analysis, appraisers should consider USPAP implications such as the following:

- DCF analysis is an additional tool that should be used in the context of *one or more* other approaches.
- The appraiser is responsible for controlling input that is consistent with market evidence and prevailing market attitudes.
- The DCF analysis should be supported by market-derived data using assumptions that are both market- and property-specific.
- The appraiser should cite the name and version of the software and provide a brief description of the methods and assumptions inherent in the software.
- The appraiser should account for and reflect those items and forces that affect the revenue, expenses, and ultimate earning capacity of the real estate and represent a forecast of events that would be considered likely within a specific market.
- The appraiser should test and check for errors in the DCF analysis.
- Standards Rule 1-1(b) states that, in developing a real property appraisal, an appraiser must not commit a substantial error of omission or commission that significantly affects the appraisal.[3]

Calculating the Present Value of Energy Savings Using a Financial Calculator

Residential appraisers may use a financial calculator such as the HP-12C to develop the present value of the cash flow. The HP-12C keystrokes are provided in Exhibit 4.5. The estimate of energy saved in a HERS Index report is credible support for new or proposed construction. For existing homes, proving the energy savings can be done by reviewing energy bills compared to those of other similar-sized

---

3.   *Uniform Standards of Professional Appraisal Practice*, 2014-2015 ed., U-71.

Strengths:

- DCF analysis reflects how market participants think about the time value of money.
- The method has been used by appraisers for commercial properties and has proven to be reliable if applied with good data.
- Present value is easily developed with current online software for homeowners and other real estate professionals. For example, PV Value is a free online software tool used for developing the DCF of energy produced for solar PV systems (available from Sandia National Laboratories at http://energy.sandia.gov and discussed in depth in Chapter 6 of this book). Also, a number of solar calculators that provide energy production estimates, payback, and costs are available online for use in California. However, they may not be a true reflection of the payback or costs for a new system.* The California tools should be reviewed for credibility and understood before being relied on for developing market value opinions, as should be done with all tools.
- The present value of energy savings was used in the Fannie Mae/Freddie Mac Energy Addendum form. Therefore, it is a method that has been used by the secondary market for many years.

Weaknesses:

- If the input data is not market driven, the result may not be credible.
- Not all buyers and sellers understand the time value of money and may not be able to use an HP-12C, although that does not render this method inappropriate.

Reasons Underwriters May Reject This Method:

- Inputs have either no support or support that is not credible.
- DCF analysis is used without a secondary method to provide a test of reasonableness.
- The underwriter does not understand the concept because the analysis is not clearly communicated in the appraisal report.

* California Energy Commission and California Public Utilities Commission, www.gosolarcalifornia.org/tools/calculators.php.

Exhibit 4.5	Determining Energy Savings with a Financial Calculator
HP-12C Calculations for DCF of Energy Savings	**Sample Support for Input**
[f] [clear] [FIN] (using payment at the beginning or [g] 7 keys)	Clears the calculator
20 years [g] [n] (payments are based on monthly savings; therefore, pressing the blue [g] key prior to pressing [n] shows 240 (20 × 12))	Based on the estimate of life of energy-efficient items from the Marshall & Swift *Residential Cost Handbook*
5% [i]	· Based on the current equity loan rate · This is higher than the first mortgage rate to allow for a shorter period · This rate more closely resembles the residential buyer's thinking
$100 monthly utility savings - [PMT]	Energy savings based on HERS Rater Report included in Addenda of the appraisal report
[PV] - results in $2,100	

Present value of energy savings: $2,100

Test of reasonableness by depreciated cost: $3,400

homes in the general area. If actual bills are used, the bills should be reviewed and the occupants interviewed to ensure that the bills reflect normal occupant use.

Fannie Mae's 2013 *Selling Guide* suggests using the present value of the energy saved discounted over the useful life of the improvement and comparing that value to the cost of the improvement to determine if the improvement is cost effective.[4] This guide's reference to the method validates its use. However, a test of reasonableness should be applied by using a secondary method. If an appraiser uses an HP-12C calculator to develop the present value, a simple table similar to what is shown in Exhibit 4.5 should be included in the report to help the reader follow the analysis.

Paired Data Analysis

Paired data analysis is the preferred method for supporting adjustments. In an ideal world, paired data analysis provides good evidence of the market's reaction to a particular element of comparison such as a garage, porch, solar PV system, or other feature found in a property that is compared by buyers in the market. However, the high-performance house is breaking new ground in many markets. Limited sales exist to develop paired data analyses in many markets. However, paired sales data from other areas with similar climate and market characteristics could be applied to the subject market. Using a paired sale from another market requires an appraiser to communicate the similarities of the other market to the client so that he or she understands the relevance.

Appraisers and underwriters prefer the paired data analysis method. However, if the market data is not available to develop a credible result, the method becomes much less applicable. This method requires sales that are similar in most physical and locational characteristics except for one isolated feature. The difference in the prices paid is attributed to that feature. In the following hypothetical example, the feature in question is energy efficiency or all of the features of a green property lumped together into one whole, as illustrated in Exhibit 4.6. Other tests of reasonableness might include the depreciated cost or present value of energy savings.

Exhibit 4.7 models a comparison of sales of Energy Star homes to sales of code-built homes in the same neighborhood that are similar in terms of age, site value, view, and square footage. This type of paired data analysis requires a sufficient number of sales with similar attributes to develop a credible value conclusion. Too often, this type of paired data analysis is used without care given to view, location, or major site value differences, which can result in a value conclusion that is not reasonable. The comparable properties shown in the table

---

4.   *Selling Guide: Fannie Mae Single Family* (Washington, D.C.: Fannie Mae, January 17, 2013), 728. The most current version of the *Selling Guide* can be found at www.fanniemae.com/singlefamily/originating-underwriting.

Exhibit 4.6 Paired Data Analysis for Energy-Efficient Adjustment

Description	XYZ Brown Street	ABC Yellow Street
Sale date	07/20XX	06/20XX
Sale price	$274,000	$265,000
Living area (sq. ft.)	2,200	2,122
Garage	2-car, attached	2-car, attached
HERS Index rating	56	Code-built at 90

Difference attributed to energy-efficient items: $274,000 less $265,000, or $9,000

Test of reasonableness based on GRM $100 monthly savings × 110 GRM = $11,000

Exhibit 4.7 Paired Sales Study of Energy Star Homes Versus Code-Built Homes

Identifier	Full Bath	Half Bath	Beds	Sq. Ft. Bldg	Fireplace	Garage	List Price	Sale Price	Date Closed	Sold Price/ Sq. Ft.	List Price/ Sq. Ft.	Yr. Built
23415	2	1	4	2,900	1	2	$299,121	$254,000	12/23/09	$87.59	$103.15	2009
21345	3	0	4	2,927	1	2	$245,000	$235,000	4/29/10	$80.29	$83.70	2007
345706	3	0	4	2,939	1	2	$299,900	$280,561	4/30/10	$95.46	$102.04	2010
34849	3	0	4	2,939	1	2	$291,900	$280,500	4/30/10	$95.44	$99.32	2010
21385	3	0	4	2,939	1	2	$326,900	$285,000	12/11/09	$96.97	$111.23	2009
24589	2	1	4	2,950	1	2	$273,571	$243,199	5/7/10	$82.44	$92.74	2009
43787	3	0	4	2,967	1	2	$290,000	$274,000	4/6/10	$92.35	$97.74	2008
Not Energy Efficient or Green			Median 2,939				$291,900	$274,000		$92.35	$99.32	
			Mean 2,937				$289,485	$264,609		$90.08	$98.56	

Identifier	Full Bath	Half Bath	Beds	Sq. Ft. Bldg	Fireplace	Garage	List Price	Sale Price	Date Closed	Sold Price/ Sq. Ft.	List Price/ Sq. Ft.	Yr. Built
493616	3	0	4	2,939	1	2	$326,900	$297,298	12/11/09	$101.16	$111.23	2009
343967	3	0	4	2,939	1	2	$299,900	$280,561	4/30/10	$95.46	$102.04	2010
685884	3	0	4	2,941	1	2	$324,900	$277,000	12/7/09	$94.19	$110.47	2009
991557	3	0	4	2,942	1	2	$269,900	$272,400	12/30/09	$92.59	$91.74	2009
214871	3	0	4	2,942	1	2	$283,900	$270,000	12/14/09	$91.77	$96.50	2009
280826	3	0	4	2,942	1	2	$279,900	$273,000	12/17/09	$92.79	$95.14	2009
427181	3	0	4	2,942	1	2	$309,900	$290,215	4/8/10	$98.65	$105.34	2010
502555	3	0	4	2,967	1	2	$290,000	$287,000	4/6/10	$96.73	$97.74	2008
Energy Star and/or green			Median 2,942				$294,950	$278,781		$94.82	$99.89	
			Mean 2,944				$298,163	$280,934		$95.42	$101.27	

have similar square footages, years built, sale dates, and garage and bath counts. The results show a median price per square foot difference of $2.47 ($94.82 – $92.35), or a 2.6% increase in the sale prices of Energy Star homes compared to the prices of homes that are not energy efficient ($2.47/$94.82 = 2.6%). The results of this type of study should be measured against a test of reasonableness. For example, what is the additional cost of these features compared to this indication of contributory value? An indication of value that is lower than current cost or similar to depreciated cost provides further support for the credibility of the study. Note that the data presented in Exhibit 4.7 is for educational purposes only and is hypothetical.

Appraisers should verify the methodology used in the analysis prior to using the results as support for an adjustment. This type of analysis should become easier to develop as multiple listing services improve their data inputs. A robust and accurate green MLS would be a major breakthrough for appraisers to meet the secondary market's requirement to only use direct market data.

Consider a study with results that are not meaningful for appraisal purposes. A study of Energy Star homes in Fort Collins, Colorado, published in the *Journal of Sustainable Real Estate* indicated that Energy Star homes sold for $8.66 more per square foot than non–Energy Star homes.[5] However, this figure is meaningless to an appraiser because it does not indicate the price range of homes that was included in this study. An appraiser should not apply such results to a property without having full knowledge of the study and how it would apply to the property being appraised.

STRENGTHS AND WEAKNESSES OF PAIRED DATA ANALYSIS

Strengths:

- This method uses direct market data, providing good support when data is sufficient to make a true comparison.
- It is the most preferred method by the secondary mortgage market and underwriters.
- It is based on a concept that buyers and sellers use.

Weaknesses:

- When data is limited, the method may not be reliable. One paired sale does not make a market.
- It can be easily abused (as illustrated in the paired data shown in Exhibit 4.8 and the accompanying example).
- Using the Energy Star illustration of paired data averages may produce an unreliable result if outliers are not removed. The more appropriate indication is the median price.

Reasons Underwriters May Reject This Method:

- Paired sales may reflect data from an inferior or superior dataset.
- The paired data analysis is improperly applied.
- Paired sales may not be for the same feature.
- Paired sales may not be properly described and identified.

Is Paired Data Analysis Infallible?

If applied incorrectly, paired sales analysis can produce a result that is not credible. Paired data analysis can be abused and in many cases is no better understood than the alternative methods. It all comes down to the competency of the appraiser and the quality of the data.

To provide an example of a paired sales analysis gone wrong, the two sales shown in Exhibit 4.8 were paired to develop a contributory value of a solar PV system. The underwriter accepted this paired sale.

---

5.   Bryan Bloom, Mary Ellen C. Nobe, and Michael D. Nobe, "Valuing Green Home Designs: A Study of Energy Star Homes," *Journal of Sustainable Real Estate* 3, no. 1 (2011): 109-126.

Description	Comparable Sale 10	Comparable Sale 11
Sale price	$210,000	$204,000
Site size	6,534 sq. ft.	6,970 sq. ft.
Style	Ranch	Ranch
Age	52 years	52 years
Room count	6/4/2	6/4/2
Gross living area (sq. ft.)	1,428	1,428
Amenities	Fence/fireplace/patio	Fence/fireplace/patio
Other	Solar	None
Prior sale transfer	None in the past year	None in the past year

The difference is $210,000 less $204,000, or $6,000 attributed to the solar PV system.

However, the homeowner strongly opposed the methodology used for very good reasons, which are explained below. This paired sales analysis is flawed on many accounts, but it met thc lender's requirement to provide a paired sale.

Notice that Exhibit 4.8 shows no prior sales of these two properties within the last year. Research through Trulia, a public website for listing and sales data (www.trulia.com), indicated that both properties had prior transfers and were resold within the year with some upgrades prior to the second sale.

The photographs of Comparable Sale 10 show that the solar panel is used for water heating and is not a solar PV system. The age of the solar water heating system is unknown, and the equipment is not comparable to a 20-panel solar PV system that is only one year old and produces 100% of the electricity for a 1,790-square-foot structure. The cost new for this one-year-old solar PV system was $32,500, as reported in the appraisal report.

What went wrong in this paired sale analysis? Either the appraiser did not verify the sales data or did not understand the differences between solar water heating and a solar PV system that produces electricity. Homeowners, agents, builders, and underwriters have access to Trulia and other data sources to review data in an appraisal report, bul most underwriters do not have the time to do the research. However, if someone involved in the transaction did the research and found an error of fact presented in the appraisal report, that person would have good reason to appeal the appraisal with fact. The secondary mortgage market allows for appeals of appraisal reports if the factual data is incorrect. The GSEs do not allow an appraisal to be appealed simply because the estimated value is not what was expected.

Supporting Adjustments

As illustrated in the previous chapter, the appraiser's toolbox contains a diverse set of reputable techniques for developing credible opinions of value for complex properties such as high-performance houses. Appraisers and other market participants need to be reminded that those old tools are still useful today and the decision to make no adjustment (or assign a value of $0 to a difference in an element of comparison) requires as much support as making a $10,000 adjustment. In the valuation of high-performance residential properties, making no adjustment for energy-efficient materials and systems should be explained in as much detail as would be provided if the appraiser determined that a particular green feature contributed an additional $25,000 to the sale price of a property.

Case Study: Lack of Adjustments for Energy Efficiency

For example, consider a 44-year-old house in an older, established neighborhood in northern Illinois with numerous energy-efficient upgrades, such as triple pane windows, an 85% efficient gas boiler, and a 16-SEER central air unit. The homeowner applied for a refinance mortgage for the house. The appraisal report rated the property's energy efficiency as "average +" but made no adjustment for energy efficiency in the sales comparison approach, even though the energy efficiency of all the comparable sales was rated as "average." The appraisal report listed the specific energy-efficient upgrades in the subject property and stated that a positive adjustment should be made but was not because no comparable properties could be found with similar components, arguing that the market had not recognized the energy-efficient items as contributing to value and that professional standards prohibited the appraiser from making adjustments for this reason.

The appraisal report included adjustments made to the sales for bathroom count, gross living area, garages, and fireplaces. However, not one comment was made to support these adjustments. Because the appraiser had no support for an energy adjustment, it was given a zero adjustment. The owner reported that the underwriter readily accepted this report as written. However, USPAP and secondary mortgage market guidelines indicate that all adjustments must have support. The homeowner quickly saw through this illogical explanation but lost the argument with the lender.

Let us review some possible solutions to this problem. This type of issue requires the appraiser to do some additional research in order to develop a supportable value conclusion. The appraiser should be able to answer the following questions:

1. Are energy upgrades beginning to occur in this older, established neighborhood?

2. Since the energy upgrades were made more than one year ago, how much did they reduce the energy costs? The owner should be able to provide energy bills from before and after the upgrades to assist in marketing or valuing the energy aspect.

3. What was the cost of the upgrades?

4. Were the sales verified to ensure that the properties have similar energy features?

5. Do the MLS listings in this neighborhood show energy upgrades in the comment sections?

6. Were agents in this market area surveyed to gain knowledge of the desires of potential buyers in this neighborhood?

The answers to these questions could lead the appraiser to make a more defensible argument. If energy upgrades being made to older homes is a trend in this neighborhood, the appraiser could reliably state that market participants are seeking energy upgrades and should describe this trend in the neighborhood section of the appraisal report. Identifying the trend is part of building a case for the analysis. The trend toward energy upgrades may be supported by MLS listings showing comments on energy upgrades in the narrative comment sections. Typically, sales agents list the items that buyers in a particular neighborhood are seeking in the narrative comments fields.

Showing the cost savings of the upgrades would provide a basis for developing an adjustment. In the scenario above, the appraiser made an adjustment of zero, which requires as much support according to USPAP as an adjustment of a higher value. Verification of the sales with a party involved in the transaction, such as the listing or selling agent, may reveal the thinking of market participants on this feature. Combining verification of the sales with a survey of sales agents to gain knowledge of what buyers are seeking in these older houses can provide valuable information for supporting opinions.

CALL TO ACTION

Appraisers need to communicate with agents to stay in touch with the changing trends that they experience from working with buyers and sellers in the market.

In this case, asking the following questions of sales agents could provide useful information that would support an adjustment:

1. Do buyers ask about energy bills in this neighborhood?
2. Do buyers want houses with newer energy-efficient windows?
3. What percentage of homes in this neighborhood have had new energy-efficient windows and other energy upgrades? (A call to the building department might reveal a pattern of replacement window permits in a given neighborhood.)
4. Do houses with energy upgrades sell more quickly or for more than houses without energy upgrades?

If the sales agents reveal that a trend of energy upgrades is occurring in the neighborhood, it is important to report this information in the neighborhood section of the appraisal report, as shown in Exhibit 5.1. This builds a case for the development of an adjustment. Too often, the underwriter rejects adjustments because appraisers have not built their cases.

If a form report has insufficient space for the type of narrative shown in Exhibit 5.1, you can insert a comment that states "See Text Addendum." This is the place on the URAR form where the story begins. When underwriters read this sort of neighborhood description, they expect some analysis of energy upgrades in the sales comparison approach section of the report.

If a neighborhood shows a trend of energy upgrades, houses without energy upgrades will begin to experience penalties in the market. In cases when the desires of buyers change and the market changes to meet those demands, the houses that are not updated may not reflect the highest and best use of the property as improved. The highest and best use may become "as improved with energy upgrades." If the SAVE Act passes, this may happen quickly in neighborhoods where houses are not energy efficient because the energy bills that would be included in the debt ratio may make these homes less affordable. (The SAVE Act, which stands for Sensible Accounting to Value Energy, is a bipartisan Senate bill supported by business, real estate, energy, and environmental groups that would make energy-efficient property features more affordable by allowing average-income buyers to qualify for larger loan amounts.[1])

Exhibit 5.1	Sample Comments on Changing Neighborhood Trends in an Appraisal Report

Market Conditions: *The MLS listings show a growing trend of energy upgrades made to houses in this older, established neighborhood. Of the 12 comparable sales that occurred in the last year, six show new low-E windows, high-efficiency HVAC, and/or upgraded insulation. The sales with energy upgrades reflect shorter marketing times and prices at the upper end of the data range. A survey of agents working in this neighborhood indicates that buyers prefer houses with energy upgrades, with new windows being the top priority.*

1. Lisa Provost, "Making 'Green' More Affordable," *The New York Times* (June 27, 2013), www.nytimes.com/2013/06/30/realestate/making-green-more-affordable.html.

How Reliable Are the Estimated Energy Costs in a HERS Index Report?

Energy modelers use software to develop their analyses and predictions of energy use and ratings. The software most commonly used by third-party certifiers is REM/*Rate*. REM/*Rate* is residential energy analysis, code compliance, and rating software developed for Home Energy Rating System (HERS) providers. This software calculates heating, cooling, hot water, lighting, and appliance energy loads, consumption, and costs for new and existing single-family and multifamily homes and adjusts for the climatic conditions of the specific area.[2]

Appraisers, sales agents, underwriters, and even some of the participants in the secondary mortgage markets question the use of the Home Energy Rating System (HERS) Index report's estimated energy costs on new or proposed construction as the basis of an energy adjustment. Better support for an appraiser's conclusions can come from energy study data like the following comparisons of estimated energy costs using the HERS Index to actual energy bills. You would not expect estimated costs and actual figures to be exact for a number of reasons, including variations in weather, number of occupants, occupant lifestyles, maintenance levels of equipment, and plug loads not envisioned in the model. The modeling software uses occupancy levels based on the number of bedrooms. The software considers the number of bedrooms plus one as the number of occupants. For instance, if the house has four bedrooms, the energy modeling software assumes the house has five occupants.

Energy costs have been studied for the following four areas:

- Riverhead, New York
- Greenville, South Carolina
- Portland, Maine
- Denver, Colorado

A summary of conclusions from the study follows the data from each area.

In Exhibit 5.2, the third-party certifier used the REM/*Rate* energy modeling software that uses 30-year average weather data from the nearest weather station in Riverhead, New York. The New York study indicates that the energy modeling estimates are *higher* than actual usage. The difference is attributed to the lifestyles of the occupants, unpredicted weather conditions, and various mechanical measures. The tracking of these four homes dispels the common complaint that the energy bill estimated by the modelers is too low. Some appraisers choose not to use these numbers in developing value for fear of overvaluing the features related to energy efficiency. However, this tracking data does not support the theory that energy estimates are too low.

Addison Homes in Greenville, South Carolina (www.addison-homes.com), provided the tracking information in Exhibit 5.3. Todd

---

2. More information on this software can be found at www.archenergy.com/products/remrate.

Exhibit 5.2   New York Study Data

Identifier	House Design/ HERS Index	Occupants	10/14/2011 to 10/15/2012 Electric Bill	Weather Normalized Expenditure Compared to REM/*Rate* Model	Thermostat Setting
A–Nuvision	1-story, detached	2 adults/ 3 children	$2,305.06	-5%	72–winter 70–summer
B–Hudson Passive Project	1-story, detached	2 adults/ 2 large dogs	$1,082.39	-38%	70–year-round
C–Domus House	2-story, attached	1 adult	$1,665.81	-20%	72–winter 69-72–summer

Exhibit 5.3   South Carolina Study Data

Identifier	HERS Index	Rating Date	Living Area	Occupants	Dates of Annual Energy Bill	Amounts of Annual Energy Bill	HERS Projected Annual Energy Bill	HERS Projection Compared to Actual Usage
A-	HERS 63	Nov. 2010	2,425 sq. ft	2 adults	July 2012– June 2013	$1,044.62	$1,398	HERS is 34% higher
B-	HERS 60	Jan. 2011	3,721 sq. ft	2 adults	June 2012– May 2013	$1,995.31	$1,884	HERS is 5.5% lower
C-	HERS 50	Jan. 2009	3,802 sq. ft.	2 adults	June 2012– May 2013	$875.00	$1,144	HERS is 30.7% higher
D-	HERS 41	Aug. 2008	4,256 sq. ft.	2 adults	Nov. 2011– Nov. 2012	$1,832.55	$1,299	HERS is 29% lower
E	HERS 51	Nov. 2010	3,300 sq. ft.	2 adults	June 2011– June 2013	$1,214.80 (avg.)	$1,352	HERS is 11.3% highor

Usher, the builder, was the 2012 National Association of Home Builders Master Certified Green Professional of the Year and holds the Leadership in Energy and Environmental Design (LEED) AP credential. Three out of five of the HERS energy estimates were above the actual bills, and two HERS energy estimates were below the actual bill. This tracking data indicates that the HERS energy estimates are typically higher than the actual energy usage. The occupancy number is lower on all the houses than was envisioned in the modeling, which may have contributed to a higher HERS estimate than the actual billing.

Theresa Foster, an associate broker and appraiser of Dan Anderson Real Estate, Inc., from the Portland, Maine, area, provided the tracking data in Exhibit 5.4. The energy modeler used REM/*Rate* software. The energy tracking data from Maine indicates that the HERS report estimates are higher than the actual figures.

Sean Smith of Sean Smith Construction, Inc. (www.seansmithco. com), a builder in the Denver area, provided the energy tracking data on the property shown in Exhibit 5.5. The tracking data in this table is different from the other tracking data presented for this

Table 5.4   Maine Study Data

Identifier	HERS Index	Rating Date	Living Area	Occupants	Dates of Annual Energy Bill	Amounts of Annual Energy Bill	HERS Projected Annual Energy Bill	HERS Projection Compared to Actual Usage
A-	HERS 58	Sept. 2010	1,632 sq. ft.	2 adults	July 2011– July 2013	$2,229.89	$2,694	HERS is 20% higher
B-	HERS 56	Jan. 2012	1,452 sq. ft.	2 adults	August 2012– July 2013	$2,512.80	$2,573	HERS is 2.4% higher
C-	HERS 52	Mar. 2009	2,340 sq. ft.	2 adults	July 2011– July 2013	$2,329.31	$2,689	HERS is 15% higher

Exhibit 5.5   Colorado Study Data

Identifier	HERS Index	Rating Date	Living Area	Occupants	Dates of Annual Energy Bill	Amounts of Annual Energy Bill	HERS Projected Annual Energy Bill	HERS Projection Compared to Actual Usage
A-	HERS 26	June 2011	4,640 sq. ft.	2 adults/ 2 children	August 2011– Nov. 2012	$621.02 (avg.) + $528 for solar PV costs = $1,149.02	$1,066	HERS is 7% lower

study because the property illustrated in this exhibit has a prepaid 6.11-kilowatt solar PV system. The property owners paid $5,400 up front for the lease of the solar PV system, for an average lease cost of $22.50 per month over the term of the lease ($5,400/240 months = $22.50 per month). To make a better comparison, the $5,400 paid up front should be spread out over the term of the lease, and the annual cost over the term of the lease should be added to the energy costs ($5,400/20 year term = $270 annually or $22.50 monthly lease costs, which means $270 in additional annual costs for energy).

A full HERS report is often crucial to understanding estimates. For example, the Colorado tracking data illustrates why appraisers should review the energy modeling report carefully to identify what was included in the report. When using data like that presented here, the actual number of occupants compared to the number assumed in the HERS report should be considered. The appraiser should also factor in whether the solar PV system was considered in the HERS report. If not, the HERS energy use or savings data will be unreliable.

Studies and Surveys to Support the Contributory Value of Features

There are a number of studies on green homes and energy efficiency, and many more will surely follow in the years to come. Of the studies and white papers that are available, the majority are academic in nature or lacking the degree of due diligence that a valuation professional would typically require to validate conclusions. Before relying on these studies, consider the following points:

- There is a difference between a peer-reviewed study and other types of studies. Typically, a peer-reviewed study is published in an established academic or professional journal and is generally not funded by the industry or anyone with something to gain in the outcome.

- If a study is not peer-reviewed, the funding source should be researched and any potential vested (financial or otherwise) interest in the study's outcome on the part of the funding source should be considered.

- A study could be considered to be "published" even if it was only informally posted on a personal website, such as a blog. Consider whether significant checks and balances were in place in the process of getting the study published.

- Research all online studies and sources to ensure that the credentials and motivations of the authors are credible. Just because a website publishes an online journal does not automatically make it a credible source.

- If the results of a study are used to make an adjustment, the appraisers and their clients need to understand the methodology used (as stated in USPAP) because it could be argued that the appraisers are relying on the work of others by using a study for the sole support for an adjustment. For example, some studies use advanced statistical methods that are beyond the skill set of many appraisers, and these appraisers would not be qualified to decide if the authors of the study used such methods correctly. The bottom line is that if you do not understand the study and could not explain it to your client or the state appraisal board, you should avoid using it in an appraisal. Therefore, most statistics-based studies should be used only as back-up or background data to keep in your workfile.

- Statistical models, even those that draw from strong data sets, have limited utility for appraisals. At best, studies that use statistical models can only point out strong correlations between property prices and features. The appraisal process should be a property-specific study including direct correlation between the home price and the features for that given market. If the result of the appraisal process was simply an average price based on a dataset in the same location, there would be little need for appraisers.

After reviewing these points, it becomes clear that most studies are primarily useful as back-up support for other methods. Conducting your own study or survey is more credible than relying on a study that you may not understand. If you conducted your own study, share it with *The Appraisal Journal*; this will add credibility to the results once your peers vet it.

The following are inquiries that I have actually received and are good examples of the typical questions asked by numerous market participants:

- "I am searching for data or research indicating the value of the positive impact on residences that install or retrofit a 500% efficient geothermal system in lieu of a standard 80-92% efficiency furnace. I thought that, for every dollar saved per year, the home value would go up by X amount. In fact, I thought this might mean that $X saved per year translates to an $X increase in home value."

- "Is it true that the "20:1 theory" is a good rule of thumb for measuring the value of solar PV energy production? I heard that the "Nevin study" published by the Appraisal Institute supports this theory."[3]

Both of these common inquiries are based on a study that was not actually performed on geothermal or solar PV systems. These inquiries point out how easily a study's results can be interpreted incorrectly. The inquiring parties have heard that energy-efficient items can be valued based on the theory discussed in the study. Some websites even quote this theory and apply it to all types of energy features. An underwriter in Florida recently reported that this study is being used as the sole support for energy efficiency in a growing number of appraisal reports.

The resources listed in Exhibit 5.6 should be carefully studied prior to use and reference in your appraisal work. Note that the "Nevin study" is the first item in the list.

These studies offer data on green label premiums, green costs, and mortgage default rates. An underwriter would most likely reject the use of a single study's result as the basis for an energy or green adjustment, and would be right in doing so. *The Impact of Photovoltaic Systems on Market Value and Marketability* is the only study that uses standard appraisal methodology and that would be useful for supporting adjustments for solar PV systems in the Denver area.

It is the responsibility of the appraiser to build a case and present tests of reasonableness for any studies used. When building the case for using such a study, the following questions should be answered in the appraisal report for the underwriter's review:

- Was the study conducted by a real estate appraiser?
- What type of professional authored the study (appraiser, agent, academic, government agency)?
- Was the study peer-reviewed?
- What is the source of funding?

---

3. Rick Nevin and Gregory Watson, "Evidence of Rational Market Valuations for Home Energy Efficiency," *The Appraisal Journal* (October 1998): 401-409. Note that the Appraisal Institute did not fund or endorse this study; the article was simply published by the Appraisal Institute in *The Appraisal Journal.*

Exhibit 5.6   Green Resources to Be Used with Caution

"Evidence of Rational Market Valuations for Home Energy Efficiency," also known as the "20:1 theory" or "Nevin study"
- By Rick Nevin and Gregory Watson
- Published in the October 1998 issue of *The Appraisal Journal*

Area of Focus:	Residential energy-efficient features, such as insulation and mechanicals
Usefulness to Appraisers:	This study was conducted during prior economic times and was not done on solar PV systems, even though it is often referenced by solar sales teams. Note that appraisers are strongly encouraged to avoid using this study as support for an adjustment unless current local data exists to support the same analysis for the specific energy feature being valued.

Assessing the Market Impacts of Third Party Certification on Residential Properties
- By Ann Griffin of Earth Advantage, with Ben Kaufman of Green Works Realty and Sterling Hamilton of Hamilton Investments, LLC
- Dated May 29, 2009

Area of Focus:	Sales of green-certified homes vs. sales of noncertified homes in Seattle, Wshington, and Portland, Oregon
Usefulness to Appraisers:	This study concludes that green-certified homes sold for a premium of 3% to 5% in the Portland metropolitan area and 9.6% in the Seattle metropolitan area during the time period studied. Applying these percentages to other market areas would be inappropriate without further evidence from the appraiser's specific market area. Appraisers were involved in the review or methodology used. The results fall within the range of additional costs for green features as reported by national cost services.

Home Energy Efficiency and Mortgage Risks
- By Nikhil Kaza, Roberto G. Quercia, and Chao Yue Tian of the Department of City and Regional Planning, University of North Carolina Center for Community Capital
- Dated February 17, 2013

Area of Focus:	The findings of this study indicate that default and prepayment risks are lower in energy-efficient homes by as much as one-third.
Usefulness to Appraisers:	This report does not provide a basis for adjustments in residential appraisal reports.

Green Home Building Survey
- By McGraw-Hill Construction
- Dated December, 2011

Area of Focus:	This study indicates that the incremental costs of green housing decreased to 7% in 2011 as compared to 11% in 2006 and 10% in 2008.
Usefulness to Appraisers:	The data provides information on green cost trends in the United States. This data can be useful in explaining why current costs may be less than what owners have paid in years past.

SmartMarket Report: New and Remodeled Green Homes: Transforming the Residential Marketplace
- By McGraw-Hill Construction
- Dated 2012

Area of Focus:	According to this report, an expected five-fold increase in green building from 2011 to 2016 will consist of 29% to 38% of market share. The publication further reports that builders and remodelers with substantial green experience show a 5% increase in income for green construction as compared to buyers who are willing to pay 6% more for green homes.
Usefulness to Appraisers:	This study can provide secondary support for cost premiums quoted from local and national cost services.

Residential Cost Handbook
- By Marshall & Swift/Boeckh
- Dated 2013

Area of Focus:	This handbook indicates that the additional cost for green features in residential buildings is 3% to 20%.
Usefulness to Appraisers:	National cost service data provides good support for local cost data.

The Value of the Green Labels in the California Housing Market
- By Nils Kok of the University of California—Berkeley and Matthew E. Kahn of the University of California—Los Angeles
- Dated July, 2012

Area of Focus:	This study indicates that green-certified homes sell for 9% more than comparable, non-labeled homes. This study focused on houses that averaged around $400,000; therefore, the 9% premium indicates a $34,000 premium. The authors state that this premium is correlated to the environmental ideology of the area as measured by the number of registered hybrid cars. They also note that the premium for green homes is higher in hotter climates, which may be due to the high cost of air-conditioning.
Usefulness to Appraisers:	Note that this study was completed by academics and was not vetted by appraisers. While it is helpful for appraisers be aware of the study, it should not be used as the basis for adjustments unless the methodology is understood and the appraiser is working in the same market area and within the same price range.

Exhibit 5.6   Green Resources to Be Used with Caution *(continued)*

The annual "Cost Vs. Value" report published in Hanley-Wood's *Remodeling* magazine
· Available at www.remodeling.hw.net

Area of Focus:	This well-established annual report on upgrade payback covers more than 10 years and 35 major or minor remodels. It provides a review of the relationship of upgrade costs to market value and provides construction costs for detailed demonstration projects.
Usefulness to Appraisers:	Robust statistical modeling is used to determine the degree of accuracy for this annual report. Appraisers should consider the relevance of this study to their markets and only consider this as secondary data as long as the methodology used is understood.

The Resale Market Value of Residential Solar Photovoltaics: A Summary of Literature and Insight into Current Value Perceptions
· By Mary Beth McCabe of Sun Marketing and the University of San Diego and Liz Merry of Verve Solar and the University of California Extension, Berkeley
· Dated 2008

Area of Focus:	This report describes eight previous studies of solar valuation, presents results from an online survey of solar homeowners and buyers, and provides examples of how the "20:1 theory" is currently used in solar marketing. The study concludes that current research on the resale value of solar PV systems does not demonstrate that there is a definite tie between installing a PV system and recouping a higher home selling price. A study of actual resale data is needed to clarify the instances in which solar PV systems have resale values and the amount of value that PV system owners might expect.
Usefulness to Appraisers:	Appraisers should review this study for an overview of the eight studies quoted. The authors make valid points from an objective viewpoint. This study does not provide support for adjustments for green or energy-efficient features.

The Cost of Value: PV and Property Taxes
· By the American Solar Energy Society
· Dated 2012
· Available at http://ases.conference-services.net/resources/252/2859/pdf/SOLAR2012_0356_full%20paper.pdf

Area of Focus:	This report provides a study of current methods of assessing and exempting solar PV systems in 15 states.
Usefulness to Appraisers:	Reviewing the methods used by property assessors to value solar PV systems provides insight into how others value solar PV systems. This study provides information on the methodology used by appraisers' peers.

"Valuing Green Home Designs: A Study of Energy Star Homes"
· By Bryan Bloom, Mary Ellen C. Nobe, and Michael D. Nobe
· Published in the *Journal of Sustainable Real Estate*, vol. 3, no.1
· Dated 2011

Area of Focus:	The authors of this article studied Energy Star–labeled homes in Fort Collins, Colorado, and conclude that Energy Star homes sell for $8.66 per square foot more than non-labeled homes. The study was conducted on homes built after 1999 with sales dates between 1999 and 2005 and uses hedonic modeling to arrive at the conclusion.
Usefulness to Appraisers:	This study does not provide the price range of houses studied needed to convert its findings into a percentage. This study is not useful in supporting adjustments made for premiums for Energy Star homes because of the methodology used, lack of peer review, and unspecified price range of homes studied.

The Impact of Photovoltaic Systems on Market Value and Marketability
· Written by Lisa K. Desmarais, SRA, and vetted by appraisers
· Published by the Colorado Energy Office
· Dated October, 2013

Area of Focus:	This study analyzes the effect of solar PV systems on home prices. The author, an appraiser, analyzed 30 homes in the northwest Denver metropolitan area with sale prices between $200,000 and $680,000. This study uses the three approaches to value and concludes that 22 of the 30 case studies indicated that PV systems contributed $1,400 to $2,600 per kilowatt to the sales prices of the properties.
Usefulness to Appraisers:	This study indicates that seller-owned PV systems typically increase market value and almost always decrease marketing time. This appraiser-driven study uses recognized methodology and can be easily understood by appraisers. It can provide good support for adjustments for solar PV systems in the Denver metropolitan area. More local studies of this nature are needed to foster a better understanding of the value of solar PV systems in different market areas.

- Did the funding source have something to gain from the outcome of the study?
- Is the study from a market area with similar demographics to the property you are appraising?
- Can you explain the methodology used in the analysis?

It should not be up to the underwriter to research the data used in an appraisal report to prove its validity. These questions provide a basis for judging the credibility of the results. A study should provide additional support for the traditional methods of developing value from market data.

Why Aren't Studies Conducted by Appraisers?

After I interviewed a number of appraisers, it became apparent to me that most appraisers do not have access to the funds or skills for grant writing that are available in academia. However, a study conducted by professional appraisers who actively appraise in the market would be much more influential in the market than one conducted by academics.

The majority of the existing studies use public records or commercial databases that retrieve data from public records. Appraisers are well aware of how credible that data can be when most public record sources do not identify green features or updates made to the property since the prior sale. Compounding that problem is the failure of proprietary databases to interface with each other and provide one central place to document the high-performance characteristics of houses. It is no wonder that most studies are based on assumptions and hedonic regression modeling rather than the verification of a significant number of high-performance property sales compared to a similar number of non-green property sales.

In many studies that use resales to prove the value of a feature such as a solar PV system, the authors often admit that they assume that the difference between the prior sale and the current sale is attributed to the solar PV system or other feature being isolated. However, solar installers indicate that owners often replace the roof and make other energy improvements prior to installing the solar PV system, all of which improve the performance of the property.

Conducting a study of resales to isolate the contributory value of a feature requires a review of each sale to determine if other features were added, if the sale was an arm's-length transaction, if concessions were included in the sale, and if there was a change in market conditions from the date of the original sale to the current sale. Answering these questions takes time, and it requires verification through more than public records and knowledge of the local market. For example, *The Impact of Photovoltaic Systems on Market Value and Marketability*, the 2013 Colorado study listed in Exhibit 5.6, verified the paired sales used in the analysis.

Exhibit 5.7 shows an example of how data can be misleading when additional knowledge of the sales or market area is lacking. It would be dangerous for an appraiser to choose the 33% as a market conditions adjustment for a 2011 sale compared to a value as of 2012. A local appraiser should know and explain that this market had a large number of foreclosures and short sales between 2008 and 2011, with a smaller number of foreclosures and short sales occurring in 2012. If this market were studied for resales to develop the value of

MEDIAN HOME PRICES

Punta Gorda MSA	2012	% CHG 2012 vs. 2011	2011	% CHG 2011 vs. 2010	2010	% CHG 2010 vs. 2009	2009	% CHG 2009 vs. 2008	2008
January	$90,000	7%	$84,500	-17%	$102,100	3%	$99,500	-37%	$156,800
February	$90,000	-10%	$100,000	4%	$96,600	0%	$96,400	-36%	$151,300
March	$118,250	23%	$96,000	-13%	$110,600	20%	$92,200	-39%	$152,200
April	$110,000	10%	$99,950	-13%	$114,500	20%	$95,500	-33%	$143,400
May	$111,500	13%	$99,000	-5%	$103,900	7%	$97,200	-37%	$154,600
June	$110,000	10%	$99,950	-6%	$106,600	-27%	$145,600	3%	$141,000
July	$104,900	3%	$101,500	6%	$95,700	-9%	$105,000	-26%	$141,800
August	$109,950	18%	$93,000	-9%	$101,800	-1%	$103,300	-25%	$138,100
September	$118,000	20%	$98,300	8%	$90,900	-18%	$110,600	-19%	$136,900
October	$110,000	22%	$90,000	-6%	$96,200	-12%	$109,300	-10%	$121,800
November	$122,250	23%	$99,000	7%	$92,500	-8%	$100,000	2%	$97,700
December	$129,500	33%	$97,500	10%	$88,400	-21%	$111,800	9%	$102,400

Source: Charlotte County Economic Development website, http://floridasinnovationcoast.com/index.php/community_data/housing.

market change without consideration of the sales affected by foreclosures and short sales that do not meet the definition of market value sales (i.e., arm's-length transfers), the result would be unreliable. The same thing can easily happen in using this type of data to isolate a feature's contributory value if the original and current sales are not verified to confirm the details that may have affected the prices paid. About the only thing you can draw from the data in Exhibit 5.7 is that the market improved in 2012.

Case Study: Supporting a Green Feature Adjustment in an Appraisal Report

The appraisal report should start building the case for adjustments related to green features from the beginning. The appraiser should move through the sections of the report, documenting the facts that build the case for the analysis. The following example illustrates the sections of the report that should address these facts, allowing the client to understand all the green data considered and avoiding any "surprises" at the end of the report. Note that this case study is presented for educational purposes only, and the example provided is not taken from an actual appraisal report.

Neighborhood Comments

The local community is aggressively encouraging green construction. The county building department offers free consulting to builders who join the green building group. The building department provides expedited building permits and offers monthly sessions on green construction for raters and builders.

The market area has some high-performance houses but no recent sales requiring the use of code-built house sales. Resales of

FEATURE	SUBJECT	COMPARABLE SALE NO. 1	+(-) $ Adjustment	COMPARABLE SALE NO. 2	+(-) $ Adjustment	COMPARABLE SALE NO. 3	+(-) $ Adjustment
Green St Address		Brown St		Yellow St		Blue St	
Proximity to Subject		0.05 Mi W		0.75 Mi. E.		0.25 Mi NE	
Sale Price	$ 225,000	$ 215,000		$ 228,000		$ 225,000	
Sale Price/Gross Liv. Area	$ 131.73 sq. ft.	$ 120.79 sq. ft.		$ 120.00 sq. ft.		$ 116.88 sq. ft.	
Data Source(s)		MLS 56749		MLS 76438		MLS 67598	
Verification Source(s)		Agent		Agent		Agent	
VALUE ADJUSTMENTS	DESCRIPTION	DESCRIPTION	+(-) $ Adjustment	DESCRIPTION	+(-) $ Adjustment	DESCRIPTION	+(-) $ Adjustment
Sale or Financing Concessions		Conventional None		Conventional None		Conventional None	
Date of Sale/Time		2 Months ago		3 Months Ago		4 Months Ago	
Location	Quiet Street	Quiet Street		Quiet Street		Quiet Street	
Leasehold/Fee Simple	Fee Simple	Fee Simple		Fee Simple		Fee Simple	
Site	20,000 Sq.Ft.	18,000 Sq.Ft.		18,200 Sq.Ft.		17,800 Sq. Ft.	
View	Residential	Residential		Residential		Residential	
Design (Style)	Ranch	Ranch		Ranch		Ranch	
Quality of Construction	Good	Good		Good		Good	
Actual Age	Proposed	2 Yrs		1 Yr.		2 Yrs.	
Condition	Good	Good		Good		Good	
Above Grade Room Count	Total 6 / Bdrms. 3 / Baths 2	Total 7 / Bdrms. 3 / Baths 2		Total 7 / Bdrms. 3 / Baths 2		Total 7 / Bdrms. 3 / Baths 2	
Gross Living Area 45.00	1,708 sq. ft.	1,780 sq. ft.	0	1,900 sq. ft.	-8,640	1,925 sq. ft.	-9,765
Basement & Finished Rooms Below Grade	None None	None None		None None		None None	
Functional Utility	Average	Average		Average		Average	
Heating/Cooling	Hi Efficiency	Central		Central		Central	
Energy Efficient Items	HERS 58/Slr Wh	HERS 109	6,450	HERS 109	6,840	HERS 109	6,750
Garage/Carport	2-Car Garage	2-Car Garage		2-Car Garage		2-Car Garage	
Porch/Patio/Deck	Scr/Entry	Scr/Entry		Scr/Entry		Scr/Entry	
Amenities	Solar Htd Pool	Solar Htd Pool		Solar Htd Pool		Solar Htd Pool	
Green Score	Emerald	None		None		None	
Net Adjustment (Total)		[X]+ [ ]- $	6,450	[ ]+ [X]- $	1,800	[ ]+ [X]- $	3,015
Adjusted Sale Price of Comparables		Net Adj. 3.0% Gross Adj. 3.0% $	221,450	Net Adj. -0.8% Gross Adj. 6.8% $	226,200	Net Adj. -1.3% Gross Adj. 7.3% $	221,985

(side label: SALES COMPARISON APPROACH)

green or energy-efficient houses were not available. The MLS searchable green fields were implemented within the last year. It will take a few years to populate the MLS with sufficient resales to extract market support for energy efficiency.

Reconciliation of Sales Comparison Approach

Below is a summary of the reconciliation of the approaches to value for a high-performance house. (Note that the Uniform Appraisal Data (UAD) format is not used because this report is written for a variety of viewers who may not understand this format.)

The subject property is proposed construction with a preliminary green certification and Home Energy Rating System Index (HERS Index) of 58, which indicates that the subject is 51% more efficient than it would be if it were built to code like Comparable Sales 1 through 5. The builder provided the preliminary HERS Index rating of 58 for the subject's specification, and the same structure's rating would be 109 if it were built to code. Because the comparable sales are code-built houses, the HERS Index is 109 for these one- and two-year-old structures, compared to the subject's HERS Index of 58. The building department confirms the code-built HERS Index at 109 for houses

FEATURE	SUBJECT	COMPARABLE SALE NO. 4	+(-) $ Adjustment	COMPARABLE SALE NO. 5	+(-) $ Adjustment	COMPARABLE SALE NO. 6	+(-) $ Adjustment
Address	Green St	Purple St		Red St		Orange St	
Proximity to Subject		0.35 Mi S		0.55 Mi N		0.45 Mi SE	
Sale Price	$ 225,000	$ 210,000		$ 218,000		$ 245,000	
Sale Price/Gross Liv. Area	$ 131.73 sq. ft.	$ 123.46 sq. ft.		$ 122.47 sq. ft.		$ 133.88 sq. ft.	
Data Source(s)		MLS 74673		MLS 57894		MLS 62458	
Verification Source(s)		Agent		Agent		Agent	
VALUE ADJUSTMENTS	DESCRIPTION	DESCRIPTION	+(-) $ Adjustment	DESCRIPTION	+(-) $ Adjustment	DESCRIPTION	+(-) $ Adjustment
Sale or Financing		Conventional		Conventional		Active Listing	
Concessions		None		None		None	
Date of Sale/Time		2 months ago		3 months ago		Active Listing	-12,750
Location	Quiet Street	Quiet Street		Quiet Street		Quiet Street	
Leasehold/Fee Simple	Fee Simple	Fee Simple		Fee Simple		Fee Simple	
Site	20,000 Sq.Ft.	20,000 Sq.Ft.		17,500 Sq.Ft.		17,500 Sq.Ft.	
View	Residential	Residential		Residential		Residential	
Design (Style)	Ranch	Ranch		Ranch		Ranch	
Quality of Construction	Good	Good		Good		Good	
Actual Age	Proposed	2 Yrs.		1 Yr		1 Yr	
Condition	Good	Good		Good		Good	
Above Grade Room Count	Total 6 / Bdrms 3 / Baths 2	Total 6 / Bdrms 3 / Baths 2		Total 7 / Bdrms 3 / Baths 2		Total 7 / Bdrms 4 / Baths 2	
Gross Living Area 45.00	1,708 sq. ft.	1,701 sq. ft.	0	1,780 sq. ft.	0	1,830 sq. ft.	-5,490
Basement & Finished	None	None		None		None	
Rooms Below Grade	None	None		None		None	
Functional Utility	Average	Average		Average		Average	
Heating/Cooling	Hi Efficiency	Central		Central		Central	
Energy Efficient Items	HERS 58/Slr Wh	HERS 109	6,300	HERS 109	6,540	HERS 55/Slr WH	
Garage/Carport	2-Car Garage	2-Car Garage		2-Car Garage		2-Car Garage	
Porch/Patio/Deck	Scr/Entry	Scr/Entry		Scr/Entry		Scr/Entry	
Amenities	Solar Htd Pool	Solar Htd Pool		Solar Htd Pool		Solar Htd Pool	
Green Score	Emerald	None		None		Emerald	
Net Adjustment (Total)		[X] + [ ] - $	6,300	[X] + [ ] - $	6,540	[ ] + [X] - $	18,240
Adjusted Sale Price of Comparables		Net Adj. 3.0% Gross Adj. 3.0% $	216,300	Net Adj. 3.0% Gross Adj. 3.0% $	224,540	Net Adj. -7.4% Gross Adj. 7.4% $	226,760

built one and two years ago. The HERS Index report estimate is $69 per month in energy savings for the subject property.

Four methods support the energy-efficiency adjustment in the sales comparison approach grid. Because of the limited sales of high-performance houses, a paired sales analysis is not possible. The energy-efficiency adjustment incorporates other aspects of green features; therefore, an additional adjustment for the green score is not necessary. The subject is proposed construction under contract and the sales are one- or two-year-old structures. Sales are all located in the same neighborhood, and the only adjustment on the first five sales other than energy efficiency is for gross living area (GLA) differences. The GLA adjustment is based on market extraction. The market does not show a discernible difference for 100 square feet or less of GLA.

Comparable Sale 6 is a green house that is most similar to the subject. It is adjusted for its status as a listing based on the sale-to-list ratio in this area. The adjusted listing supports the upper value range presented by this dataset; however, it is the only property in this dataset matching the subject property's green and energy-efficient characteristics.

In the absence of paired sales from the local market, alternative methods provide support for the energy-efficiency adjustment, which includes the green features. Because there is such limited market data, it is impossible to identify a separate adjustment for green features. The green features all attribute to the energy-efficiency of the subject property; therefore, the adjustment is most appropriate under this category.

The 2013 Marshall & Swift/Boeckh *Residential Cost Handbook* provides a measure of the difference in cost between the standard and upgraded energy features. The "good" energy rating cost is $3.74 per square foot compared to the "average" energy rating of $1.82 per square foot. This makes for a difference of $1.92, which is divided by the $77.57 base cost per square foot for a 1,700-sq.-ft. house to yield a 2.5% adjustment

	Test of Reasonableness	
Method	**Brief Analysis of Findings**	**% Adjustment Implied**
Study from similar area	Green-certified homes sold for 3% to 5% more than non-green homes.	3%-5%
Gross rent multiplier	110 *GRM* × $69 savings/month = $7,590, $7,590/$225,000 (subject sale price) = 3.3% The *GRM* is based on local data supporting the *GRM* at 110 based on a similarly priced sale.	3.3%
Present value of energy savings using a DCF	$69 monthly savings @ 5% discount rate based on a 5% rate similar to the second mortgage or equity loan for a 20-year period. The 20-year estimate is based on the typical useful life of energy components (Marshall & Swift *Res. Cost Handbook*, 2013). The present value is $10,455/$225,000 cost new = 4.6%.	4.6%
Marshall & Swift/ Boeckh *Res. Cost Handbook*	A good energy rating $3.74 − $1.82 for an average energy rating = $1.92, $1.92/$77.57 base cost per square foot for 1,700-sq.-ft. structure = 2.5%.	2.5%
Neighborhood price range	The indicated value of the subject, after making this adjustment, remains within the indicated value range reported in the neighborhood section at $175,000 to $275,000.	

Reconciliation of Indicators

The four methods summarized in the table above indicate a range of 2.5% to 5% for energy-efficient and green features. The data deserves the most weight at 3%. A 3% line-item adjustment is well within the secondary mortgage market guidelines and supported by these well-recognized methods. The 3% adjustment is applied to the sales with a HERS Index of 109. Although this is an across-the-board adjustment, it is based on a comparison of code-built to HERS 58 and is therefore appropriate. The listing does not require an adjustment for energy efficiency because it has a similar HERS Index rating.

Case Study Observations

The methods used and reconciliation illustrate the appropriate use of the tools from the appraisal toolbox. Using tests of reasonableness adds credibility to the results. Paired data analysis was not possible in this case. Rather than applying a zero adjustment, the appraiser used other methods that have been widely accepted in the market for many years and are taught in qualifying education courses. Using one of the methods alone might not be convincing to the underwriter, but it is difficult to argue with the results when two or more methods are analyzed and reconciled.

Using more than one method provides a much more convincing analysis than using one paired sale. The market is imperfect, and therefore the sales data is imperfect. A wise appraiser will take additional steps to support the conclusion. However, this type of analysis is not usually achieved in 48 hours and at the lowest appraisal fee.

What Message Do Underwriters Have to Convey to Appraisers?

Underwriter Survey

I approached a number of underwriters and asked them to provide comments on energy-efficient appraisals as well as what they would like to see in appraisal reports to support energy-efficient adjustments. The following paraphrased responses I received should provide no surprises.

Response A
"Better comparables needed. However, appraisers are very slow to provide *any* value to energy- efficient items. I saw–for the first time ever–an adjustment for a heat pump on an appraisal yesterday. The subject and two comparables had heat pumps; one comparable did not. The appraiser made an adjustment for it. I think it is going to take a very long time for them to be able to place value (market reaction) to energy efficiency because as yet I don't think it is a driving force behind the purchase.

If you had a neighborhood of all newly built homes that all had various energy-efficient items, it would be easier. However, in this market and at this point, adjustments for a newly built home with energy-efficient items in an area surrounded by older homes that do not have energy-efficient items will just give you comparables that have adjustments outside acceptable guidelines. Therefore, the appraisers are not going to make those adjustments when the house is comparable in almost every over way and conforms otherwise."

Response B

"I have honestly not seen any support provided in the rare cases that I have seen appraisals of properties with high-performance features. It would be nice to see financial calculations showing the savings over the typical holding period."

Response C

"A recent appraisal indicated a $5,000 adjustment for an energy-efficient furnace with no support or comment on the basis for the adjustment. The adjustment is excessive without support."

The Good News

In another five years, we will not be having this same problem because data to support adjustments will be more abundant. Until more high-performance houses sell and appear in databases, appraisers will be required to use all the tools in their toolboxes. The good news is that we already have many tools we can use.

Residential Green and Energy Efficient Addendum Form

SITE   WATER   ENERGY   AIR QUALITY   MATERIALS   MAINTENANCE

A New Tool for Appraisers

The Appraisal Institute released Form 820.04, the Residential Green and Energy Efficient Addendum, in September of 2011 and an update to the form in March of 2013. It is clear that a high-performance property presents a challenge and increases the amount of writing time required when using the URAR form or the Appraisal Institute's Summary Appraisal Report–Residential Form 100.[1] The addendum, which was created as part of the Appraisal Institute's AI Reports series of forms, can be used with the URAR form or Form 100.

The Appraisal Institute's objectives for creating the addendum include the following:

- Provide one central place in a report for green and energy-efficient features
- Standardize the reporting process
- Organize and expand the description sections of the residential forms
- Provide a basis for comparable sale selection
- Proactively prepare appraisers for the proposed legislation known as the Sensible Accounting to Value Energy (SAVE) Act

The addendum is part of a proactive movement to prepare for the SAVE Act, which may become law in the near future. According to the Institute for Market Transformation (IMT), the passing of the SAVE Act will add an "E" for energy costs to the PITI–principal, interest, taxes, and insurance–currently used in qualifying a buyer for a loan. The act will require an average monthly utility cost to be developed and included in the debt ratio. Water and location-based transportation costs are envisioned as future phases of the act.[2]

---

1. The Appraisal Institute developed Form 100 for use with residential property appraisals that are not related to lending. It is included in most appraisal software packages as Form 100.04 AI.
2. Institute for Market Transformation, www.imt.org/save-act.

Keeping the six elements of green building (site, water efficiency, energy efficiency, indoor air quality, materials, and operations and maintenance) in mind, the addendum moves through the building description, addressing the areas that are not included on the residential appraisal forms. The main categories addressed on the addendum, represented by large "blocks" on the form, are

- Green features
- Energy-efficient items
- Solar panels
- Location/site
- Incentives

The addendum is not a systematic guide for appraising or identifying a green or energy-efficient house. However, keep in mind that the first step in competency is education. Education can be gained through classroom or online study or by working with others who have already gained competency. Identifying or verifying that a property is green or energy efficient without having a basic understanding of the six elements of green building is impossible. The addendum references the documents and information that are necessary to describe the "shade" of green and degree of energy efficiency of the subject property. However, the addendum is not a replacement for green valuation education.

Benefits to the Appraisal Process

The addendum supplements energy and green description features and assists in identifying characteristics of comparable sales and potential adjustments in the sales comparison approach. The addendum also provides resources for identifying incentives that offset the current costs of green features. It ends with a glossary of terms with web addresses for researching additional information. The glossary is necessary for informing the readers, clients, and reviewers of the appraisal report and addendum of the green-related terminology that may be foreign to them. Appraisers often find it necessary to add additional glossary terms to appraisal reports.

Benefits to Underwriting

Consider a mortgage underwriter's checklist of items to review on an appraisal form and his or her limited amount of time available to review the report. If the green features are not standardized, it is easy to understand why underwriters often reject premiums or adjustments for green or energy-efficient items. Underwriters who have 15 to 30 minutes to review and either accept or reject an appraisal should welcome the standardization offered by the addendum. If they must read text addenda that narratively describes green features, the importance of the features is often overlooked. If the Residential Green and Energy Efficient Addendum form is included with the URAR form, this quickly alerts underwriters that the property is not standard and deserves a closer review. Inclusion of the completed addendum form also standardizes the reporting process, making the review process easier.

Who Can Complete the Addendum?

Builders, homeowners, third-party certifiers, agents, or appraisers can complete the addendum form, which is available to anyone on the Appraisal Institute's website. The person with the most knowledge of a property's green features is the most appropriate person to complete the addendum. The form should be provided to the lender, appraiser, and sales agent to be used in the appraisal ordering and development process or in marketing the property. Agents should attach the addendum to the MLS for appraisers and buyers to access. A blank copy of the addendum is shown in Exhibit 6.1.

Documents Needed to Complete the Addendum Form

Exhibit 6.2 provides a list of documents that are necessary to accurately complete the addendum and describe the features of a high-performance home. The builder should provide copies of these documents to the lender, appraiser, real estate agent, and homeowner. Copies should also be kept with the house upon transfer to a new owner. Reminding buyers to keep these documents will be invaluable on resale.

Keep in mind that USPAP has specific requirements that relate to relying on the work of others when using energy modeling analysis in valuation. According to Standards Rule 2-3 of the 2014-2015 edition of USPAP,

> When a signing appraiser(s) has relied on work done by appraisers and others who do not sign the certification, the signing appraiser is responsible for the decision to rely on their work. The signing appraiser(s) is required to have a reasonable basis for believing that those individuals performing the work are competent. The signing appraiser(s) also must have no reason to doubt that the work of those individuals is credible.[3]

An appraiser may need to question the author of an energy modeling report to ensure an understanding of the document. Appraisers are not energy modelers or builders. Therefore, they must work with professionals in the field or take educational classes to gain knowledge of the documents used in the field.

Using a comparison table like the sample provided in Exhibit 6.3 is a great way to compare features and benefits concisely for the benefit of buyers, agents, underwriters, and other appraisers. Appraisers should identify the specific building code used because not all areas have adopted the International Energy Conservation Code (IECC).

Preparing a comparison table of the major differences between a high-performance house and a code-built house is a great tool to use for analysis and marketing. It quickly identifies major differences that will be found when these construction types are compared.

---

3. Standards Rule 2-3, *Uniform Standards of Professional Appraisal Practice*, 2014-2015 ed. (Washington D.C.: The Appraisal Foundation, 2013), U-27.

Exhibit 6.1   Residential Green and Energy Efficient Addendum

Client File #:			Appraisal File #:	

AI Reports®

Form 820.04*

Residential Green and Energy Efficient Addendum

Client:

Subject Property:

City:	State:	Zip:

Additional resources to aid in the valuation of green properties and the completion of this form can be found at
http://www.appraisalinstitute.org/education/green_energy_addendum.aspx

The appraiser hereby certifies that the information provided within this addendum:

- has been considered in the appraiser's development of the appraisal of the subject property only for the client and intended user(s) identified in the appraisal report and only for the intended use stated in the report.
- is not provided by the appraiser for any other purpose and should not be relied upon by parties other than those identified by the appraiser as the client or intended user(s) in the report.
- is the result of the appraiser's routine inspection of and inquiries about the subject property's green and energy efficient features. Extraordinary assumption: Data provided herein is assumed to be accurate and if found to be in error could alter the appraiser's opinions or conclusions.
- is not made as a representation or as a warranty as to the efficiency, quality, function, operability, reliability or cost savings of the reported items or of the subject property in general, and this addendum should not be relied upon for such assessments.

Green Building: The practice of creating structures and using processes that are environmentally responsible and resource-efficient throughout a building's lifecycle from siting to design, construction, operation, maintenance, renovation, and deconstruction. This practice expands and complements the classic building design concerns of economy, utility, durability, and comfort.[1] High Performance building and green building are often used interchangeably.

Six Elements of Green Building: A green building has attributes that fall into the six elements of green building known as (1) site, (2) water, (3) energy, (4) materials, (5) indoor air quality, and (6) maintenance and operation. A Green Building will be energy efficient but an energy efficient building is not synonymous with Green Building.

Green Features

The following items are considered within the appraised value of the subject property:

Certification	Year Certified:	Certifying Organization: ☐ Home Innovation Research Labs (ICC-700) ☐ USGBC (LEED) ☐ Other:	☐ Verification Reviewed on site	☐ Certification attached to this report
Rating	Score:	☐ LEED Certified: ☐ LEED Silver ☐ LEED Gold ☐ LEED Platinum		
		☐ ICC-700 *National Green Building Standard* Certified: ☐ Bronze ☐ Silver ☐ Gold ☐ Emerald		
		Green Certifying Organization URL (website)		
Additions	Explain any additions or changes made to the structure since it was certified:			
	Do changes require recertification to verify rating is still applicable? ☐ Yes ☐ No			
Comments Attach the rating worksheet that provides the ratings for each element to provide a better understanding of the features. The worksheet will assist in comparing the subject to sales rated by different organizations.	If a property is built green but not formally certified, it still deserves proper description and analysis to value the features. The market analysis is of the structure's physical, economic, and locational attributes and not an analysis of its label alone.			

The objective of this Addendum is to standardize the communication of the high performing features of residential properties. Identifying the features not found on the 1004 form provides a basis for comparable selection and analysis of the features. Builders, contractors, homeowners, and third party verifiers are encouraged to complete this Addendum and present to appraisers, agents, lenders, and homeowners.

---

[1] U.S. Environmental Protection Agency at www.epa.gov/greenbuildings/pubs/about.htm.

*NOTICE: The Appraisal Institute publishes this form for use by appraisers where the appraiser deems use of the form appropriate. Depending on the assignment, the appraiser may need to provide additional data, analysis and work product not called for in this form. The Appraisal Institute plays no role in completing the form and disclaims any responsibility for the data, analysis or any other work product provided by the individual appraiser(s).
AI Reports® AI-820.04 Residential Green and Energy Efficient Addendum   © Appraisal Institute 2013, All Rights Reserved   January 2013

Exhibit 6.1   Residential Green and Energy Efficient Addendum *(continued)*

Client:		Client File #:	
Subject Property:		Appraisal File #:	

ENERGY EFFICIENT ITEMS

The following items are considered within the appraised value of the subject property:

Insulation	☐ Fiberglass Blown-In ☐ Foam Insulation ☐ Cellulose ☐ Fiberglass Batt Insulation ☐ Other (Describe): ☐ Basement Insulation (Describe): ☐ HERS Insulation Installed Rating: ☐ 1 ☐ 2 ☐ 3 (See Glossary)	R-Value: ☐ Walls ☐ Ceiling ☐ Floor
Envelope	Envelope Tightness: Unit: ☐ CFM25 ☐ CFM50 ☐ ACH50 ☐ ACHnatural ☐ Envelope Tightness based on Blower Door Test	
Water Efficiency	☐ Reclaimed Water System (Explain): ☐ Cistern - Size: Gallons ☐ Greywater reuse system ☐ WaterSense® fixtures ☐ Rain Barrels Provide Irrigation	Location of cistern:

Windows	☐ ENERGY STAR®	☐ Low E	☐ High Impact	☐ Storm	☐ Double Pane ☐ Triple Pane	☐ Tinted	☐ Solar Shades
Day Lighting	☐ Skylights - #:	☐ Solar Tubes - #:	☐ Other (Explain):				☐ ENERGY STAR Light Fixtures

Appliances	ENERGY STAR® Appliances: ☐ Dishwasher ☐ Refrigerator ☐ Other:	Water Heater: ☐ Solar ☐ Heat Pump ☐ Tankless ☐ Coil Size: Gal.	Appliance Energy Source: ☐ Propane ☐ Electric ☐ Natural Gas ☐ Other (Describe):	
HVAC (Describe in Comments Area)	☐ High Efficiency HVAC SEER: Efficiency Rating: % AFUE* % *Annual Fuel-Utilization Efficiency	☐ Heat Pump Efficiency Rating: COP: HSPF: SEER: EER:	☐ Thermostat/Controllers	☐ Passive Solar (Defined in Glossary)
	☐ Programmable Thermostat		☐ Radiant Floor Heat	☐ Geothermal
Energy Rating	☐ ENERGY STAR ®Home - Version: ☐ Other (Describe): Home Energy Score (HES) (Score range 1-10): ☐ Certification Attached			
Indoor Air Quality	☐ Indoor Air PLUS Package	☐ Energy Recovery Ventilator Unit or Whole Building Ventilation System		☐ Non Toxic Pest Control
HERS Information	Rating:	Monthly Energy Savings on Rating: $		Date Rated:
Utility Costs	Average Annual Utility Cost: $ per month based on:			# of Occupants:
Energy Audit	☐ Infrared Photograph Attached Has an energy audit/rating been performed on the subject property? ☐ Yes ☐ No ☐ Unknown If yes, comment on work completed as result of audit.			
Comments (Include source for information provided in this section) Attach documents or reference them in your workfile The energy element is the most measurable element of green or high performance housing.	Information was provided by:			

*NOTICE: The Appraisal Institute publishes this form for use by appraisers where the appraiser deems use of the form appropriate. Depending on the assignment, the appraiser may need to provide additional data, analysis and work product not called for in this form. The Appraisal Institute plays no role in completing the form and disclaims any responsibility for the data, analysis or any other work product provided by the individual appraiser(s).

AI Reports® AI-820.04 Residential Green and Energy Efficient Addendum   © Appraisal Institute 2013, All Rights Reserved   January 2013

Exhibit 6.1   Residential Green and Energy Efficient Addendum *(continued)*

Client:		Client File #:	
Subject Property:		Appraisal File #:	

Solar Panels

The following items are considered within the appraised value of the subject property:

Description	Array #1	☐ Leased ☐ Owned	Array #2	☐ Leased ☐ Owned	Description	Solar Thermal Water Heating System
kW (size)					If Active System - type	☐Direct ☐ Indirect
Manufacturer of Panels					If Passive System - type	☐ Integral collector ☐ Thermosyphon
Warranty on Panels					Storage Tank Size	# Gallons:
Age of Panels					Collector Type	☐ Flat-Plat Collector ☐ Integral Collector ☐ Evacuated-Tube Solar
Energy Production kWh per Array						
Source for Energy Production Estimate					Back-Up System	☐ Conventional Water Htr ☐ Tankless On Demand ☐ Tankless Heat Pump
Location (Roof, Ground, Etc.)					Age of System	
Tilt/Slope for Array					Warranty Term	
Azimuth per Array					Manufacturer	
Age of Inverter(s)					Solar Energy Factor (SEF) (Rating range 1 to 11 - higher number is more efficient)	
Manufacturer						
Warranty Term						

Name of Utility Company:		Cost per kWh charged by Company: $ /kWh	

Comments (Discuss incentives available for new panels, condition of current panels, and any maintenance issues. If leased, provide the lease terms.) A free online tool and manual for valuing the energy production of the Solar PV System is available at www.pvvalue.com Download the PV Value™ Manual for explanation of the solar terms on this form and inputs used in the PV Value Tool.	Discuss source of information and define other renewable energy sources, such as wind, hydropower, biomass power, etc.

Exhibit 6.1 Residential Green and Energy Efficient Addendum *(continued)*

Client:		Client File #:	
Subject Property:		Appraisal File #:	

Location - Site

The following items are considered within the appraised value of the subject property:

Walk Score	Score:	Source: (Example: http://www.walkscore.com)		
Public Transportation	☐ Bus – Distance: Blocks	☐ Train – Distance: Blocks	☐ Subway – Distance: Blocks	
Site	Orientation - front faces: ☐ East/West ☐ North/South	Landscaping: ☐ Water Efficient ☐ Natural		
Comments				

Incentives - Amount of Incentive and Terms

The following items are considered within the appraised value of the subject property:

Federal	
State	
Local	
Source (For example www.dsireusa.org)	
Comments Incentives offset cost and should be reported in the cost approach section of the report. Incentives are typically not a sales comparison approach concession since they do not transfer with the property.	

Completed by:_____ Title:_____ Date:_____

need to provide additional data, analysis and work product not called for in this form. The Appraisal Institute plays no role in completing the form and disclaims any responsibility for the data, analysis or any other work product provided by the individual appraiser(s).
AI Reports® AI-820.04 Residential Green and Energy Efficient Addendum   © Appraisal Institute 2013, All Rights Reserved   January 2013

Exhibit 6.1   Residential Green and Energy Efficient Addendum *(continued)*

Client:		Client File #:	
Subject Property:		Appraisal File #:	

Residential Green and Energy Efficient Addendum
Glossary and Resources

ICC-700 National Green Building Standard (NGBS): An ANSI-approved residential green building standard developed by the National Association of Home Builders (NAHB) and the International Code Council (ICC). It is applicable to single and multifamily projects, renovations and additions and residential land development. To comply, all buildings must incorporate sustainable lot development techniques and address energy, water & material resource efficiency and indoor environmental quality. Also, all owners must be educated about building operation and maintenance. Certification to the NGBS is provided by the **Home Innovation Research Labs.** http://www.nahb.org/page.aspx/generic/sectionID=2510 or http://www.homeinnovation.com/

LEED: Leadership in Energy and Environmental Design is redefining the way we think about the places where we live, work and learn. As an internationally recognized mark of excellence, LEED provides building owners and operators with a framework for identifying and implementing practical and measurable green building design, construction, operations and maintenance solutions. http://www.usgbc.org/DisplayPage.aspx?CMSPageID=1988

Energy Star®: ENERGY STAR certified new homes must meet strict energy efficiency guidelines set by the U.S. Environmental Protection Agency. These homes are independently verified to be at least 15% more energy efficient than homes built to the 2009 International Energy Conservation Code (IECC), and feature additional measures that deliver a total energy efficiency improvement of up to 30 percent compared to typical new homes and even more compared to most resale homes. http://www.energystar.gov/index.cfm?c=new_homes.hm_index

Home Energy Score (HES): The Home Energy Score is similar to a vehicle's mile-per-gallon rating. The Home Energy Score allows homeowners to compare the energy performance of their homes to other homes in the area. It also provides homeowners with suggestions for improving their homes' efficiency.

The process starts with a home energy assessor collecting energy information during a brief home walk-through. The assessor then scores the home on a scale of 1 to 10, with a score of 10 indicating that the home has excellent energy performance. A score of 1 indicates that the home needs extensive energy improvements. In addition to providing the score, the home energy assessor provides the homeowner with a list of recommended energy improvements and the associated cost savings estimates. http://www1.eere.energy.gov/buildings/residential/hes_index.html

HERS Index: The Home Energy Rating System (HERS) Index is the Industry Standard by which a home's energy efficiency is measured. It's also the nationally recognized system for inspecting and calculating a home's energy performance. http://www.resnet.us/hers-index This Index is assessed by a qualified third party certifier based on the physical characteristics of the house. The energy estimates from this assessment may vary depending on the lifestyle of the occupants, increasing utility expenses, and changes in the maintenance or characteristics of the energy features.

Building Envelope: The building envelope is everything that separates the building's interior from the exterior. This includes the foundation, exterior walls, roof, doors and windows.

Geothermal: A geothermal heat pump uses the constant below ground temperature of soil or water to heat and cool your home. http://energy.gov/energysaver/articles/geothermal-heat-pumps

Low-E: Low emittance indicates a coating is added to the glass surface. The coating allows visible light to pass through the glass while stopping the radiant heat energy from the sun and heat sources in the building from passing through the glass. Approximately 40% of the sun's harmful ultra violet rays are blocked and insulation enhanced.

Whole Building Ventilation System: A whole building ventilation system assists in a controlled movement of air in tight envelope construction and may include air-purifying systems. Whole building ventilation equipment is often a part of the forced air heating or cooling systems.

Energy Recovery Ventilation System: Often called Heat Recovery Ventilators (HRV). These systems replenish the indoor air without wasting all the energy already used to heat the indoor air. In some climates, these systems are also used to handle water vapor in the incoming air.

Passive Solar: Passive solar is technology for using sunlight to light and heat buildings with no circulating fluid or energy conversion system. http://rredc.nrel.gov/solar/glossary A complete passive solar building design has the following five elements: (1) aperture (collector) (2) absorber (3) thermal mass (4) distribution (5) control. http://www.nrel.gov/docs/fy01osti/27954.pdf

SEER: Seasonal energy efficiency ratio - The higher the SEER rating, the more energy efficient the equipment is. A higher SEER can result in lower energy costs. http://www.energystar.gov/index.cfm?c=tax_credits.tx_definitions&dts=ssps,mcs,seer.eer

Water Sense: EPA released its Final Version 1.1 WaterSense New Home Specification. This specification will be effective January 1, 2013 and establishes the criteria for new homes labeled under the WaterSense program and is applicable to newly constructed single-family and multi-family homes. http://www.epa.gov/watersense/new_homes/homes_final.html

Water Heaters: Solar, Heat Pump, Tankless On Demand or Tankless Coil water heaters are described at the following location: http://energy.gov/energysaver/articles/solar-water-heaters.

Green Certifying Organizations: A partial list of organizations can be found at: http://www.usgbc.org/ShowFile.aspx?DocumentID=2001

HERS Insulation Installed Rating: Rating 1 is the best with 3 the lowest rating. http://www.resnet.us/standards/Enhancements_to_National_Rating_Standards.pdf

SAVE Act: The SAVE Act is proposed legislation to improve the accuracy of mortgage underwriting used by federal mortgage agencies by ensuring that energy costs are included in the underwriting process. http://www.imt.org/finance-and-leasing/save-act

- HERS Index rating and full accompanying report
- Home Energy Score (HES) rating (applies to existing homes only)
- Green score and worksheet that shows points awarded for the score
- Copy of Energy Star certificate (if applicable)
- Plans and specifications
- Cost breakdown that shows premiums awarded for green features (cost above code-built)
- Incentives for high-performance features that offset costs
- Comparison table of code-built versus high-performance structures

Exhibit 6.3   Sample Comparison of a Code-Built House and a High-Performance House

Feature	2012 Code-Built House	High-Performance House
HERS Index	90	56
Estimated monthly utility bill	$145	$95
Wind load	150	165
Window type	Double pane	Low-E
HVAC/air	14 SEER*/95% efficient	19 SEER/98% efficient
Incentives/rebates	$0	$2,500 for HVAC 19 SEER

* SEER is defined later in this chapter.

Logic suggests that lending institutions should be more willing to place a mortgage on the property with the lower monthly expenses. Exhibit 6.3 indicates a $50 per month difference in the utility bill alone, which should mean that more money is left each month for paying the mortgage. A study completed in 2013 by the University of North Carolina indicated that default and prepayment risks are lower in energy-efficient homes by as much as one-third.[4]

Completing the Form

Completing the Appraisal Institute's Residential Green and Energy Efficient Addendum is a straightforward process of researching and describing the subject property's green features, energy-efficient items, solar panels, location or site, and incentives. The addendum includes other sections that do not require input from the person filling out the form but that are relevant to the reader, such as the appraiser's certification and the objective statement.

Appraiser's Certification

The first section of the addendum provides some general certification statements that alert readers to the intended limitations of the data presented in the form. The appraiser's certification statement ap-

---

4.   Department of City and Regional Planning, UNC Center for Community Capital, University of North Carolina at Chapel Hill, *Home Energy Efficiency and Mortgage Risks* (February 2013).

pears first and is followed by a definition of *green building* and a brief explanation of the six elements of green building. The appraiser's certification is worded as follows:

> The appraiser hereby certifies that the information provided within this addendum:
>
> - has been considered in the appraiser's development of the appraisal of the subject property only for the client and intended user(s) identified in the appraisal report and only for the intended use stated in the report.
> - is not provided by the appraiser for any other purpose and should not be relied upon by parties other than those identified by the appraiser as the client or intended user(s) in the report.
> - is the result of the appraiser's routine inspection of and inquiries about the subject property's green and energy efficient features. Extraordinary assumption: Data provided herein is assumed to be accurate and if found to be in error could alter the appraiser's opinions or conclusions.
> - is not made as a representation or as a warranty as to the efficiency, quality, function, operability, reliability or cost savings of the reported items or of the subject property in general, and this addendum should not be relied upon for such assessments.

It is always important to cover the limits of the information provided. Because appraising a high-performance house involves estimates of energy costs, details that are not usually visible to the human eye, and reliance on professional reports, appraisers must make some assumptions and remind readers that the opinions and conclusions set forth are not guarantees or warranties.

Green Features Section

The green features section of the addendum should be completed whether or not the property has been rated by a third-party certifier. If the property has a third-party certification, a copy of the certification and a worksheet outlining the points awarded should be provided along with the addendum. If the subject property is a high-performance house that has not had a third-party certification, use the comments box at the end of the green features section to address the characteristics of the house that fall within the six elements of green building. If there is not enough space in the addendum, attaching a list of the property's green features may also be helpful to the reader.

Only the national certification organizations are specifically listed in the addendum. The vast number of regional certifying organizations can be addressed by checking "other" in the certification box of the green features section and naming the certifying organization that provided the rating for the property.

For example, consider a home certified by the EarthCraft program based in Atlanta, Georgia. Because this is not a national program, the appraiser would check the "other" box under the "certifying organization" heading, provide the year the property was certified, check the appropriate box if the certification is attached, include the score, and provide the EarthCraft website address, as shown in Exhibit 6.4.

Exhibit 6.4   Green Features Section

Green Features				
The following items are considered within the appraised value of the subject property:				
Certification	Year Certified: 2006	Certifying Organization: ☐ Home Innovation Research Labs (ICC-700) ☐ USGBC (LEED) ☒ Other: EarthCraft	☐ Verification Reviewed on site	☒ Certification attached to this report
Rating	Score: Platinum	☐ LEED Certified: ☐ LEED Silver ☐ LEED Gold ☐ LEED Platinum		
		☐ ICC-700 *National Green Building Standard* Certified: ☐ Bronze ☐ Silver ☐ Gold ☐ Emerald		
		Green Certifying Organization URL (website) http://www.earthcraft.org/house		

It is important to include the year of certification because the programs change as building codes change. Therefore, if an appraiser must use comparable sales that were certified years ago but the certification program has since changed, those changes could affect comparability. The score allows the appraiser to understand the property's "shade" of green. It is important to review the scoring checklist that accompanies the certification to understand the points received in the various categories. No two certifying organizations have the same points system, and each green project is usually unique. The certification scoring checklist provides a comparison of these differences. Certification checklists are rarely provided to appraisers or agents even though they are valuable aids to understanding the property's green features.

> **CALL TO ACTION**
>
> Real estate professionals should review checklists from various green certifying organizations to gain knowledge of their different points systems. The completed checklist should be attached to the MLS for appraisers and buyers to review.

Green Certifying Organizations

The two notable national green certifying organizations listed on the addendum are

- Home Innovation Research Labs
  The certification provided by Home Innovation Research Labs is based on compliance with the ICC 700 National Green Building Standard (NGBS), a residential green building standard that was developed by the National Association of Home Builders (NAHB) and the International Code Council (ICC) and approved by the American National Standards Institute (ANSI). This certification is applicable to single-family and multifamily projects, renovations, additions, and land development. To comply, all buildings must incorporate sustainable lot development techniques and address energy, water, and material resource efficiency and indoor environmental quality. In addition, all owners must be educated about building operations and maintenance.

- US Green Building Council (USGBC)
  The USGBC's Leadership in Energy and Environmental Design (LEED) certification is the most widely recognized set of criteria for green building. LEED has had a major effect on the

general public's awareness of sustainability issues in the built environment. LEED provides building owners and operators with a framework for identifying and implementing practical and measurable green building design, construction, operations, and maintenance features.

Over 100 other certifying organizations exist in the United States, and the addendum and this text cannot possibly include them all. Exhibit 6.5 lists a number of programs that have certified large numbers of houses or that are growing in popularity, and Exhibit 6.6 maps several regional programs. Notice that not all certifying programs are equal. For instance, some programs require pre-drywall verification and others do not. Also, some organizations such as Energy Star address only the energy efficiency, water efficiency, and indoor air quality elements of green building. Knowing the requirements of the programs in a specific area assists appraisers, sales agents, and buyers in comparing properties with certifications from different green organizations.

The information provided in Exhibit 6.5 was researched and confirmed with each organization listed as of July 2013. Appraisers and agents can develop their own tables similar to the one in Exhibit 6.5, focusing on the organizations serving their local areas. This type of comparison can be useful in understanding and communicating the requirements of the various programs.

Green Features Comment Samples

Exhibit 6.7 shows some details that might be included in the comments box of the green features section. Use this area of the form to clarify or explain new programs or details about the property that may affect the reader's understanding of its green features.

The comments in Exhibit 6.7 point the reader to the worksheet that should be attached. If the green certification rating is based on a builder's speculation or model home and not a review of the plans and specifications or actual rating of the property being appraised, that fact should be clearly disclosed. Some production builders are completing the addendum using a model home as the basis for all the houses they build of that same model. Appraisers should approach this type of rating with caution by clarifying the facts regarding the ratings with builders.

Objective of the Addendum

A statement of the objective of the addendum appears at the bottom of the first page of the form, directly below the green features section. The statement provides clarification as to who may complete the addendum. The wording from the addendum is as follows:

> The objective of this Addendum is to standardize the communication of the high performing features of residential properties. Identifying the features not found on the 1004 form provides a basis for comparable selection and analysis of the features. Builders, contractors, homeowners, and third party verifiers are encouraged to complete this Addendum and present to appraisers, agents, lenders, and homeowners.

Exhibit 6.5   Green Certification Programs

Program Name	Sponsor Type	What Is Rated	Where Prevalent	Number of Units Certified	New or Existing	Verified by Third Party?	Pre-Drywall Inspection?	Performance Testing?
Energy Star	US EPA (government)	Energy efficiency	Nationwide + Puerto Rico and Guam	1,400,000+ through first qtr. 2013	New + gut rehab	Yes	Required	Not required
HERS/ HERS II	RESNET (NGO*)	Energy efficiency	Nationwide	1,300,000	New + existing	Yes	Not required	Required
Home Innovation NGBS Green Certified	Home Innovation Research Labs	Energy efficiency	Nationwide	20,242	New + renovation + retrofits	Yes	Not required	Not required
LEED-Homes	USGBC (NGO)	Sustainability	Nationwide	40,443	New + gut rehab	Yes	Required	Required
GreenPoint	Build It Green (NGO)	Sustainability	CA (primarily)	10,413 single-family (new and existing homes)/ 10,695 multifamily (new and existing homes)	New + existing	Yes	Not required	Required
Earth Advantage	Earth Advantage Institute (NGO)	Sustainability	OR and Vancouver, WA (Portland standard metro statistical area)	13,800	New only	Yes	Required	Required
Built Green	Master Builders Assoc. (builders)	Sustainability	Seattle area	14,171 since 2000	New only	Optional (4- & 5-star level only)	Not required	Not required
EarthCraft	Greater Atlanta Home Builders Association & Southface (builders/NGO)	Sustainability	Southeast	26,800	New + existing	Yes	Required	Required
EarthCents	Georgia Power	Energy efficiency	Georgia		New	Yes		Required
GreenBuilt Texas	Home Builder Association of Greater Dallas (builders)	Sustainability	Texas	8,600	New only	Yes	Required	Required
Florida Green Building Coalition (FGBC)	Florida Green Building Coalition (NGO)	Sustainability	Florida	6,436	New + existing	Yes	Required	Dependent on which credits sought in certification: HERS required for existing home certification, HERS optional for new homes
PHIUS+	Passive House Institute US	Energy efficiency	Nationwide	60	New + retrofit	Yes	Not required	Required
Ecomagination (www.ge.com/ yourhome)	General Electric and Masco Environments for Living Certified Green Program	Sustainability	Nationwide, but predominantly Florida and Texas	250	New	Yes	Required	Required

* Nonprofit green organization (NGO)

Source: Information provided as of July 2013 by each organization as listed. Note that some organizations reported their number of properties certified as a combined figure including both single-family and multifamily properties, while other organizations reported these figures separately.

Exhibit 6.6   Green Organizations Map

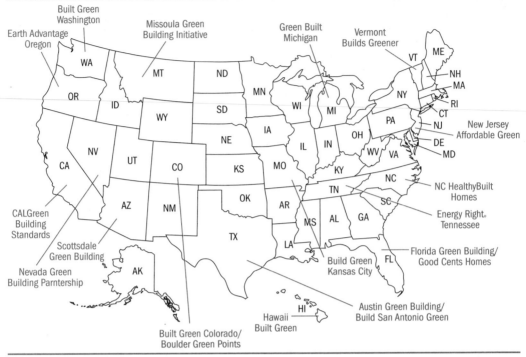

Source: National Association of Realtors' Green REsource Council, *Green 100: Real Estate for a Sustainable Future* (2011).

Exhibit 6.7   Sample Green Features Comments

Comments	
Comments Attach the rating worksheet that provides the ratings for each element to provide a better understanding of the features. The worksheet will assist in comparing the subject to sales rated by different organizations.	If a property is built green but not formally certified, it still deserves proper description and analysis to value the features. The market analysis is of the structure's physical, economic, and locational attributes and not an analysis of its label alone. The green score is preliminary based on the plans and specifications and points system to achieve the Gold award. Upon completion of the project, the final score and certification will be finalized. The point's worksheet is attached to provide an understanding of the green features proposed for this project. If you have any questions regarding the green features, you may reach the green certifier at XXX-XXX-XXXX.

Energy-Efficient Items Section

The second page of the addendum form is devoted to the items that apply to the energy-efficiency of high-performance houses. Some green properties, such as Energy Star houses, are "labeled" as such, but properties without these labels may also have similar features. The market value of the appraised property should reflect the house as built or as proposed. While the label may bring a premium, a house without a label should still be appraised based on its characteristics. This section of the addendum should be completed if the property has energy-efficient features, whether or not the house has a green label.

Insulation

There are many different types of insulation, and the R-value is used as a measure of the insulation's ability to resist heat travelling through it. (A higher R-value indicates a better thermal performance.[5]) However, many energy rating scores also take envelope tightness, mechanicals, and orientation into consideration. In the insulation section of the form, appraisers should provide verifiable information regarding the type and R-value of the insulation, including any documents that support these findings. If no information is known, *this section should be left blank.* Appraisers are not experts in this area and should only base their descriptions on verifiable reports.

The HERS Insulation Installed Rating was brought about by the number of installations that did not meet manufacturers' specifications. Good quality insulation is only as good as the installation. A rating of one is the best, and a rating of three is the lowest. The ratings (see Exhibit 6.8) should be documented with reports from qualified professionals such as energy modelers, HERS Index experts, green raters, building scientists, or Building Performance Institute (BPI) raters. Appraiser and real estate agents are not qualified energy modelers and must rely on credible reports from these qualified individuals.

Exhibit 6.8	Insulation Section of the Addendum Form

| Insulation | ☐ Fiberglass Blown-In ☒ Foam Insulation ☐ Cellulose ☐ Fiberglass Batt Insulation
☐ Other (Describe):

☐ Basement Insulation (Describe):

☐ HERS Insulation Installed Rating: ☒ 1 ☐ 2 ☐ 3 (See Glossary) | R-Value:

☒ Walls R-19
☒ Ceiling R-39
☐ Floor |

Envelope

The building envelope constitutes everything that separates the building's interior from the exterior. The tightness of the envelope and duct system is measured and reported by third-party certifiers and may be reported on the addendum form by checking one or more of the boxes listed as units in the envelope portion of the energy-efficient items section of the form and shown in Exhibit 6.9. This information can be found in HERS Index reports and other energy modeling reports.

---

5. Energy Star, "Recommended Levels of Insulation," www.energystar.gov/?c=home_sealing. hm_improvement_insulation_table.

Cubic feet per minute (CFM) measures how fast unintentional air is moving into or out of the house.[6] In reality, CFM or ACH (air changes per hour) measurements provide an indication of the rate of air exchange for any reason. These measurements are used for calculating mechanical ventilation needs and capacity, for example, as well as for measuring air exchange caused by leaks in the building envelope. A measurement per cubic feet per minute (CFM) provides an indication of the volume of air entering or leaving the building within a period of time, indicated as 25 or 50 minutes. The measurement is only relevant if the pressure is specified as 50 or 25.

Exhibit 6.9	Glossary of Building Envelope Terms
❏ CFM25	A measurement per cubic feet per minute that provides an indication of the volume of air entering or leaving the building within 25 minutes
❏ CFM50	A measurement per cubic feet per minute that provides an indication of the volume of air entering or leaving the building within 50 minutes
❏ ACH50	Air changes per hour using a pressure of 50 (or depressurization) in pascals with reference to outdoors
❏ ACHnatural	Air changes per hour with no artificial pressurization or depressurization

A home with 0.25 ACHnatural (i.e., one-quarter of the air is replaced each hour under natural conditions) is relatively airtight, as is a home that measures 1,500 CFM50. A very leaky home might have air exchange readings of 1 or more ACHnatural or 4,000 or more CFM50. However, these measurements are relative. A high CFM50 measurement is more significant in a small home, for example, and there is typically greater tolerance for leakiness in moderate climates than in extreme ones.[7]

Appraisers should ask the BPI or HERS raters to explain the envelope rating for the property. Based on the information provided by the raters, the appraiser should explain the ratings and provide the information source in the comments section at the bottom of page 2 of the addendum.

The ACH50 measurement does not equal how much the house will leak under natural conditions; instead, it measures how well a house is sealed. The lower the ACH50, the tighter the house and the less energy required for heating and cooling. Exhibit 6.11 lists ACH (air changes per hour) envelope and duct leakage (CFM–cubic feet per minute) requirements by climate zones. Appraisers can use this table to compare the ratings on properties they are appraising to code requirements in their climate zones. Many additional energy pro-

---

6.   *Building Science Principles Reference Guide*, 1st ed. (Malta, NY: Building Performance Institute, 2012), 83.

7.   Robin LeBaron (managing director, National Home Performance Council), in discussion with the author.

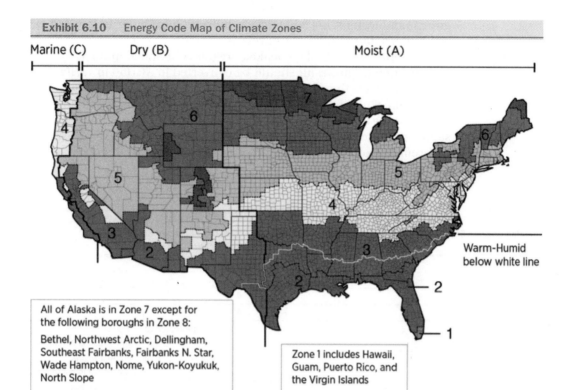

Exhibit 6.10   Energy Code Map of Climate Zones

Marine (C)   Dry (B)   Moist (A)

7

6

4

6

5

5

3

4

2

3

2

2

Warm-Humid
below white line

1

All of Alaska is in Zone 7 except for
the following boroughs in Zone 8:

Bethel, Northwest Arctic, Dellingham,
Southeast Fairbanks, Fairbanks N. Star,
Wade Hampton, Nome, Yukon-Koyukuk,
North Slope

Zone 1 includes Hawaii,
Guam, Puerto Rico, and
the Virgin Islands

Source: US Department of Energy, Building Energy Codes Program, www.energycodes.gov.

INTERNATIONAL ENERGY CONSERVATION CODE

According to the US Department of Energy, different states have adopted different editions of the International Energy Conservation Code (2003, 2006, 2009, or 2012). The recently finalized 2015 building code edition is expected to have similar efficiency requirements as the 2012 building code edition. Appraisers should review the differences among the energy codes so that they understand which code applies in the jurisdiction of the property they are appraising. Understanding the different codes is especially important if the property being appraised is a high-performance building. Comparing sales of older structures built to a code that is less stringent than the standards used to build newer high-performance structures may be comparing "apples to oranges." High-performance properties typically exceed the building code, and high-performance building requirements often increase in order to stay above code as building energy codes increase. Comparing the code ratings to the high-performance house ratings is a way to understand how much more efficient the appraised property should be. Exhibit 6.11 provides the ratings for some programs and codes.

HELPFUL HINT FOR GEORGIA APPRAISERS

The Georgia State Minimum Standard Energy Code 2011 requires the envelope and duct rating information to be placed on the building's electrical box or on the air handler for all new homes. More information can be found at www.dca.ga.gov/development/ConstructionCodes/programs/DET.asp.

grams not listed in this table have requirements similar to the 2009 or 2012 International Energy Conservation Code.

Sometimes an envelope leakage result is included in the CFM50 measurement. The result should be converted to ACH50 to verify if the house meets the code or program requirements. The example shown in Exhibit 6.12 demonstrates two different houses and how to convert their results to ACH50. Although these two homes have the same envelope leakage measurement in CFM50, they have two very different outcomes when converted to ACH50 measurements:

$$(\text{CFM50} \times 60 \text{ minutes}) / (\text{volume of the house}) = \text{ACH50}$$

Exhibit 6.11   ACH Envelope Tightness and Duct Leakage Requirements

Building Code or Energy-Efficiency Program	Envelope Tightness ACH50 Requirements	Climate Zones	Total Duct Leakage Requirements (CFM25 per 100 sq. ft.)
LEED for Homes V2008*	7	1-2	4
LEED for Homes V2008*	6	3-4	4
LEED for Homes V2008*	5	5-6	4
LEED for Homes V2008*	4	7-8	4
Energy Star V3.0*	6	1-2	4 if ducts are tested during construction 8 if ducts are tested after the house is complete
Energy Star V3.0*	5	3-4	4 if ducts are tested during construction 8 if ducts are tested after the house is complete
Energy Star V3.0*	4	5-6	4 if ducts are tested during construction 8 if ducts are tested after the house is complete
Energy Star V3.0*	3	7-8	4 if ducts are tested during construction 8 if ducts are tested after the house is complete
2012 IECC	5	1-2	4
2012 IECC	3	3-8	4
2009 IECC†	7	1-8	6 if ducts are tested during construction 12 if ducts are tested after the house is complete
2006 IECC – 2000 IECC	No requirement	1-8	No requirement
Passive House	0.6	1-8	4 if ducts are tested during construction 8 if ducts are tested after the house is complete

* For LEED and Energy Star, there are two choices for compliance: (1) the performance path or (2) the prescriptive path. The values listed are for the prescriptive path.

† For the 2009 IECC, there are two choices for compliance: (1) a visual inspection or (2) an envelope leakage test. These values are only required if the envelope leakage test is used to verify compliance.

Source: Lauren Westmoreland (LEED AP BD+C, building science trainer and specialist, Advanced Energy), in discussion with the author, November 2013.

Exhibit 6.12   Comparing "Apples to Apples" Using Envelope Leakage Results in CFM50

	Example 1	Example 2
House square footage	2,500 sq. ft.	1,200 sq. ft.
Ceiling height	9 ft.	9 ft.
House volume	22,500 ft.^{3}	9,600 ft.^{3}
Envelope leakage result	1,862 CFM50	1,862 CFM50
CFM50 conversion to ACH50	(1,862 CFM50 × 60 minutes)/ (22,500 ft.^{3}) = **4.97 ACH50**	(1,862 CFM50 × 60 minutes)/ (9,600 ft.^{3}) = **11.6 ACH50**

Appraisers are not qualified to insert the building envelope rating information in an appraisal report without relying on information from qualified professionals. For this reason, supporting documents should be attached to the appraisal report or kept in the workfile. Appraisers should become familiar with the rating and understand how to compare it to current local code ratings.

Blower Door Test

A blower door test is a diagnostic tool that provides the envelope tightness rating of a structure. The comments section at the bottom of the energy-efficient items section of the addendum form is the proper place to provide the rating from the rater's report and provide a brief explanation of it. Exhibit 6.13 shows an example of comments on envelope tightness that might be provided in this section of the addendum.

The photograph in Exhibit 6.14 shows the blower door equipment used to test the envelope tightness. Real estate professionals who have not experienced this test should contact a local HERS rater to see the test being performed. Experiencing the test in action is interesting and provides a better understanding of the technology of measuring envelope leakage.

The blower door test provides a mechanical measure of how tight the building envelope is sealed. The rater uses a Duct Blaster air duct blower to test the tightness of the ductwork and provide a rating for the duct system. The envelope and duct tightness rating can be found on HERS Index worksheets. It is worth noting that if the HVAC equipment and ducts are in the conditioned space, the duct testing is not required.

Some building envelope and duct ratings are posted on a label on the building's electrical box. While this information is helpful to appraisers and all other parties involved in the transaction, appraisers must have reason to believe the label is authentic before relying on the information.

Water Efficiency

Water efficiency is another measureable element of green building. Some communities offer a reclaimed water connection that serves the landscape watering at a lower billable rate than potable water. Water from rain barrels or cisterns can be used in areas that al-

| Exhibit 6.13 | Sample Envelope Tightness Comments |

Comments: The HERS Index report provides an envelope rating of 1.5 ACH50, which indicates that the building envelope is tighter than what is required by the 2012 building code, 3 ACH50.

| Exhibit 6.14 | Blower Door Demonstration |

Source: Energy Star, www.energystar.gov.

low reclaimed water. In areas where potable water is expensive and scarce, a reclaimed water system could save the homeowner a nice sum of money that may translate into added market value. Buyers and sellers make that determination in any individual market.

Gray water reuse systems may be connected to the lavatories, washer, or shower in a house. The waste water is reused for lawn watering. These systems have an added cost but an economic benefit as well.

Appraisers need information on these features for appropriate cost estimating of the property and analyzing any potential value added. If databases do not have searchable fields to allow appraisers to identify sales with these features, it will be impossible to develop a market contribution for gray water reuse systems.

WaterSense

The EPA released the final version of its WaterSense New Home Specification, effective as of January, 2013. This specification established the criteria for new homes labeled under the WaterSense water-efficiency program and is applicable to newly constructed single-family and multifamily homes.

Windows

It is important to know the type of window used to understand the energy rating and tightness of the building envelope. Windows have a wide range of cost based on their efficiency and overall quality. Older, existing housing with new low-E windows may sell at a premium over similar housing with older windows that are not as energy efficient. The appraiser must research data to develop an opinion of the market's view of the value contribution of newer windows, which takes us back to the problem of databases that do not identify houses with new low-E windows and thereby allow their value to be properly analyzed.

Low-E Windows

A low-E window, which is fabricated for low emittance, has a coating added to the glass surface that allows visible light to pass through while stopping radiant heat energy from the sun and heat sources in the building from passing through. Low-E windows block approximately 40% of the sun's harmful ultraviolet rays and enhance insulation.

Daylighting

Lighting, appliances, and electronics account for nearly half of the electricity usage in a typical US home, according to the Building Performance Institute. Daylighting features play an important part in lowering a home's overall electric rates. Daylighting includes skylights, solar tubes, and the appropriate placement of windows to provide natural daylight. Windows that face north and south are more favorable than ones that face east or west because the sunlight that shines on these windows is moderate and constant throughout the day, which is not the case with east- and west-facing windows.[8]

---

8. *Building Science Principles Reference Guide*, 1st ed. (Malta, NY: Building Performance Institute, 2012), 208.

Appliances

Energy-efficient appliances can reduce the energy consumption of a building and reduce off-gassing. Note, however, that a house that has Energy Star (ES) appliances is not necessarily an Energy Star-rated house. Having ES appliances does *not* by itself make a house green or energy efficient. MLS listings often indicate that a house is green-certified when, upon verification, the agent reveals that the green-certified box was only checked because the house has ES appliances.

Conventional water heating can create higher rates of energy consumption. However, the cost can be reduced by simply adding a timer. After I placed a timer on my water heater to heat water for only four hours a day, my electric bill was reduced by $20 per month. The timer quickly paid for itself. Larger families that require larger amounts of hot water will experience higher-than-normal energy bills unless they are using a timer, solar, heat pump, tankless on-demand, tankless coil, or hybrid water heater that reduces costs.

HVAC

The HVAC section of the addendum form includes space to indicate the rating of the home's HVAC system energy efficiency. Analysts use the SEER rating (described below) or the efficiency percentage to judge efficiency, depending on the area. Complete the portions of the HVAC section of the form that apply to common practice in your location.

AFUE

AFUE, or annual fuel utilization efficiency, is a measure of how efficiently a furnace or boiler converts fuel to heat, on average, over a typical year.[9]

SEER

The higher the seasonal energy-efficiency ratio (SEER) rating, the more energy efficient the equipment is. A higher SEER rating can result in lower energy costs.[10]

Passive Solar

Passive solar design uses sunlight to light and heat buildings with no circulating fluid or energy conversion system.[11] A complete passive solar building design has the following elements:

- Aperture (collector)
- Absorber
- Thermal mass
- Distribution
- Control

---

9. *Building Science Principles Reference Guide*, 239.
10. Energy Star, www.energystar.gov.
11. US Department of Energy, http://rredc.nrel.gov/solar/glossary.

Appraising passive solar houses requires appraisers to go the extra mile to find comparable sales and explain the features of passive solar design. It may be difficult for a buyer to secure lending for a passive solar house without a furnace or air conditioner because some secondary mortgage market guidelines in specific regions require furnaces. Chapter 9 of this book includes an example that illustrates buyer frustrations in Wyoming. Lending guidelines need updating to accommodate current building design and technology. Passive solar and green building techniques have been around for many years, but the guidelines of the secondary mortgage market have not kept pace.

Geothermal

A geothermal heat pump uses the constant below-ground temperature of soil or water to heat and cool a home.[12] In the northwestern part of the United States, the term *ground source heat pump* (GSHP) is used instead of *geothermal* for residential uses. It is important to know the term used in your market area and in the fields of your local MLS system.

The use of a geothermal system can significantly reduce the heating and cooling costs of a structure. Most homeowners will see a reduction of 30% to 70% in their heating and cooling costs. Some homeowners report difficulty in finding local professionals to service the systems, but they also indicate that the need for service is minimal. The systems operate more quietly than conventional systems, have an average life expectancy of 25 years, have less maintenance costs, provide hot domestic water, and have higher efficiency ratings.[13]

A geothermal system can capture reclaimed heat to use in heating domestic water. This is referred to as an *integrated design*. When building systems can be integrated, the economics of the project benefit. Although one system may cost more, it may serve more than one purpose or operate at a lower cost than the conventional option.

As part of the American Reinvestment and Recovery Act, the US federal government allows a 30% tax credit for Energy Star-qualified geothermal equipment installed before December 31, 2016. The appraisal process does not consider personal tax credits as concessions because they affect the personal tax position and not the property. However, homeowners report this incentive as one of the reasons why they considered using geothermal heating and cooling systems.

A good example of the energy efficiency of a geothermal heating and cooling system is shown in Exhibit 6.15. This table contains actual data from the homeowner of a residential property in Iowa as of June 2013. This example clearly indicates that the geothermal system is efficient and maintenance-free to date. This type of factual data should be provided in the comments box of the energy-efficient items section of the addendum. MLS data should provide searchable fields for geothermal systems and include recent energy bills to allow

---

12. US Department of Energy, http://energy.gov.
13. Enertech Global, LLC, and Geocomfort Geothermal Systems, *Homeowner's Guide to Geothermal*, revised January, 24, 2011, available for download at www.proudgreenhome.com/white-papers/5447/Homeowner-s-Guide-to-Geothermal.

Exhibit 6.15   Geothermal Data from an Iowa Home, June 2013

Living area	6,800 square feet
Age of structure	7.5 years
Number of year-round occupants	2
Heating/cooling source	Geothermal
Cost of geothermal system after incentives	$5,609 net cost when built
Range of monthly utility bill over 7.5 years	$52-$106 per month
Maintenance issues with geothermal system	None

buyers to make informed decisions. Energy bills will also aid the appraiser in developing energy-efficiency adjustments when comparing energy-efficient properties to comparable sales that may not have the same efficient features.

Energy Rating

Proposed construction projects with preliminary HERS Index ratings should be clearly identified on the addendum as preliminary and subject to a final rating upon completion. The preliminary rating is converted to a final rating once the building is completed. The appraiser should be given the preliminary rating if the appraisal is based on the plans and specifications. Upon final inspection, the final rating should be reviewed by the appraiser. If a significant difference exists between the preliminary rating and the final rating, the value may be materially affected. This may require another analysis at an additional fee. The prudent appraiser may make the identified preliminary rating an extraordinary assumption.

Energy Star Homes

Energy Star-certified new homes must meet strict energy-efficiency guidelines set by the US Environmental Protection Agency (EPA). These homes are independently verified to be at least 15% more energy efficient than homes built to the 2009 International Energy Conservation Code (IECC), and they feature additional measures that deliver a total improvement in energy efficiency of up to 30% as compared to typical new homes and even more as compared to most resale homes. Energy Star homes have HERS Index scores that appraisers should review and document in the addendum.

Home Energy Score (HES)

The Home Energy Score (HES) is similar to a vehicle's miles-per-gallon rating. This score is meant for existing homes rather than proposed or new construction. The HES is a voluntary rating that homeowners may obtain along with recommendations for improvements. The rating helps homeowners to compare the energy performance of their homes to other homes in the area. Exhibit 6.16 shows a home that currently has a score of 5 but could move up to a score of 7 with estimated 10-year savings of $3,900 based on the recommended improvements.

Exhibit 6.16   Home Energy Score

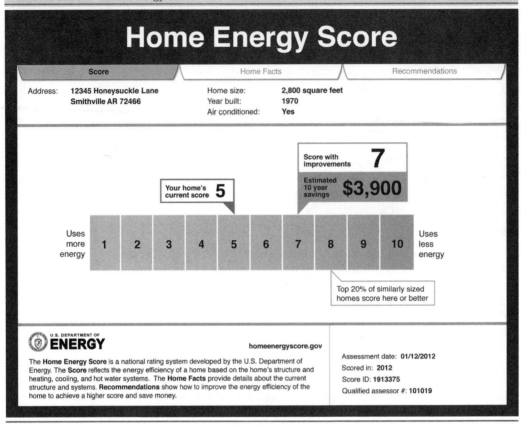

The HES rating process begins with a home energy assessor collecting energy information during a brief home walk-through. The assessor then scores the home on a scale of 1 to 10, with a score of 1 indicating that the home needs extensive energy improvements and a score of 10 indicating that the home has excellent energy performance. The rating is often called the "asset score," given standard operating assumptions. In addition to providing the score, the home energy assessor provides the homeowner with a list of recommended energy improvements and the associated cost savings estimates.

Qualified home energy assessors for this program include BPI building analysts or HERS raters. They must also pass a free, online exam given by the US Department of Energy. The estimated cost for a homeowner to obtain an HES rating is around $100. This is much lower than the cost for a HERS Index rating, which ranges from $350 to $550 for a typical home.[14]

---

14.   The typical cost range provided for a HERS Index rating is an estimate based on interviews with several HERS raters who work in different areas of the country.

Indoor Air Quality

Indoor air quality is affected by a number of factors, including construction materials, mechanicals that release off-gassing, and the tightness of the buiding envelope. A tightly sealed building envelope prevents uncontrolled air and dust pariticles from entering the living space. It also requires mechanical equipment to move air as needed using one of the following means:

- A *whole building ventilation system* assists in the controlled movement of air in tight envelope construction and may include air-purifying systems. Whole building ventilation equipment may be part of a forced-air heating or cooling system.

- An *energy recovery ventilation system,* also known as a *heat recovery ventilator* (HRV), replenishes indoor air without wasting all the energy already used to heat the indoor air. In some climates, these systems are also used to handle water vapor in the incoming air.

Nontoxic Pest Control

Nontoxic pest control systems use a nonchemical strategy of monitoring and baiting to reduce pesticides that affect air quality. Air sealing is another method used to prevent pests from entering living areas. Appraisers may not be able to identify such a system visually and should require documentation from the homeowner or builder.

HERS Information

HERS Index information is available for some green-certified and Energy Star houses. It may also be available for houses that are not certified. Obtaining a HERS Index rating is an additional non-standard or non-code cost for planned construction in most areas. This rating assists appraisers, sales agents, and buyers in measuring energy efficiency and comparing the performance of high-performance houses to that of code-built homes. To determine the HERS Index rating on a code-built house, contact the local building department and ask the engineer or energy specialist on staff. HERS Index updates occur when building or energy codes change. Therefore, HERS Indexes on local code-built houses should be checked on an annual basis.

HERS Score vs. HERS Index

The HERS Score is no longer used because it has been replaced by the HERS Index. This change occurred in 2006.[15] The HERS Index uses a house that minimally complies with the 2006 IECC and average US levels of electricity consumption for lighting and appliances as its reference points. The HERS Index requiements continually change as codes change.

---

15. Martin Holladay, "Top Ten Energy-Efficiency News Stories of the Decade: 2000-2009," *Green Building Advisor* (December 31, 2009), http://www.greenbuildingadvisor.com/blogs/dept/musings/top-ten-news-stories-decade.

The scale of the HERS Score is the opposite of the scale of the HERS Index, as shown in Exhibit 6.17. An easy way to differentiate between the two is to remember that higher is better for scores, while lower is better (or more energy efficient) for indexes. Real estate professionals must be careful when using this terminology to prevent incorrect assumptions about the energy efficiency of the structure.

HERS Index

The HERS Index is an industry standard for measuring a home's energy efficiency implemented by the Residential Energy Services Network (RESNET). It is also a nationally recognized system for inspecting and calculating a home's energy performance. This index is assessed by a qualified third-party certifier based on the physical characteristics of the house. The energy estimates from this assessment may vary depending on the lifestyle of the occupants, increasing utility expenses, and changes in the maintenance or characteristics of the energy features.

According to a RESNET report dated January 13, 2014, the number of HERS Index ratings issued in 2013 was up by 70% as compared to 2012. In 2013, 218,864 homes were HERS rated, with an average national HERS Index score of 64. This growth in the number of ratings suggests that the market is becoming more familiar with and seeking out this rating system.

The software tools for developing the HERS Index use occupant gains (British thermal units, based on energy loads) from a chart provided by RESNET or the number of bedrooms equal to the number of people occupying the home 16.5 hours per day. According to the standard, indoor temperatures are 75 degrees Fahrenheit for cooling and 70 degrees Fahrenheit for heating. The rating assumes that the master bedroom has two occupants and the other bedrooms have one occupant. For instance, a three-bedroom house would assume four occupants. If the three-bedroom house has less than four occupants, the estimated energy use and costs may exceed the actual amounts, depending on occupant behavior.[16]

Exhibits 6.18 and 6.19 show samples of an Energy Star (ES) certificate and rating sheet. The rating certificate provides many details itemized on the addendum. Documents such as these,

---

Exhibit 6.17   HERS Index vs. HERS Score

The HERS Index is like a golf score: the **lower** the score (or rating), the more energy-efficient the building.

The HERS Score (prior to 2006) was like a bowling score: the **higher** the score (or rating), the more energy-efficient the building.

---

16. *Mortgage Industry National Home Energy Rating Systems Standards* (Oceanside, CA: RESNET, 2013), www.resnet.us/standards/RESNET_Mortgage_Industry_National_HERS_Standards.pdf.

Exhibit 6.18 Energy Star Certificate

An ENERGY STAR® Version 2 Qualified Home

This home built at

XX#1234

by XXX Homes, Inc.

has been verified by Inspection 3rd Party an independent professional or organization,
to meet or exceed strict energy efficiency guidelines
set by the U.S. Environmental Protection Agency.

HERS Index: 58

5/04/XX

Sam Rashkin
National Director
ENERGY STAR for Homes

www.energystar.gov

REM/Rate - Residential Energy Analysis and Rating Software v12.93

Exhibit 6.19 Energy Star Home Energy Rating Certificate

Home Energy Rating Certificate

XXXXX, St XXXXX

5 Stars Plus

Uniform Energy Rating System | **Confirmed Rating** Energy Efficient

1 Star	1 Star Plus	2 Stars	2 Stars Plus	3 Stars	3 Stars Plus	4 Stars	4 Stars Plus	5 Stars	5 Stars Plus
500-401	400-301	300-251	250-201	200-151	150-101	100-91	90-86	85-71	70 or Less

HERS Index:	58	Efficient Home Comparison:	42% Better

General Information

Conditioned Area:	1800 sq. ft.	House Type:	Single-family detached
Conditioned Volume:	21264 cubic ft.	Foundation:	Slab
Bedrooms:	3		

Mechanical Systems Features

Air-source heat pump:	Electric, Htg: 8.5 HSPF, Clg: 15.0 SEER.
Water Heating:	Conventional, Electric, 0.91 EF, 50.0 Gal.
Duct Leakage to Outside:	0.00 CFM.
Ventilation System:	Exhaust Only: 63 cfm, 20.0 watts.
Programmable Thermostat:	Heating: Yes Cooling: Yes

Building Shell Features

Ceiling Flat:	NA	Exposed Floor:	NA
Vaulted Ceiling:	U-0.047	Window Type:	Double/LoE - Wd*
Above Grade Walls:	R-13	Infiltration:	
Foundation Walls:	NA	Rate:	Htg: 289 Clg: 289 CFM50
Slab:	R-5.0 Edge, R-0.0 Under	Method:	Blower door test

Lights and Appliance Features

Percent Fluorescent Pin-Based:	0.00	Clothes Dryer Fuel:	Electric
Percent Fluorescent CFL:	100.00	Range/Oven Fuel:	Electric
Refrigerator (kWh/yr):	506.00	Ceiling Fan (cfm/Watt):	0.00
Dishwasher Energy Factor:	0.67		

The Home Energy Rating Standard Disclosure for this home is available from the rating provider.

REM/Rate - Residential Energy Analysis and Rating Software v12.93
This information does not constitute any warranty of energy cost or savings.
© 1985-2011 Architectural Energy Corporation, Boulder, Colorado.

Rating Number: XXX
Certified Energy Rater:
Rating Date:05/01/XX
Rating Ordered For:

Estimated Annual Energy Cost
Confirmed Rating

Use	MMBtu	Cost	Percent
Heating	12.1	$305	25%
Cooling	3.8	$99	8%
Hot Water	11.0	$280	23%
Lights/Appliances	19.1	$487	39%
Photovoltaics	-0.0	$-0	-0%
Service Charges		$67	5%
Total		$1238	100%

This home meets or exceeds the minimum criteria for all of the following:

MD - Rater
PO Box XXX
XXX, ST
Rater@mail.com

Certified Energy Rater

---

including the estimated monthly energy savings, should be attached to the addendum form. The estimated monthly energy savings can be used in developing the energy adjustment.

The date the property was certified by ES is important because the program is continually updating the rating system as building codes upgrade. Appraisers may be required to use ES home sales that have different versions of the ES criteria. The certificate shown in Exhibit 6.18 refers to a certification under Version 2 of the ES standard. Appraisers should identify this version number on the addendum. Analyzing the possible effect that the rating version has on the property requires knowledge of the differences between the rating standard's versions. However, this information may be difficult to obtain in some areas.

If a home is rated by ES, a paper trail should support the rating. If the owner has lost the paperwork, verification of the information may be possible through a local ES rater. A database for public use is crucial for buyers, agents, and appraisers to gather the necessary information to make informed decisions. RESNET implemented their database to document HERS-rated homes beginning in July 2012, but only raters and builders are allowed to access this data. Houses rated prior to this date would not be identified in this database.

Notice that in Exhibit 6.19 the house is rated 5+ stars, which is the best rating possible. All ES rating certificates show the HERS Index and the number of stars based on the index.

Based on this energy estimate and the Fannie Mae/Freddie Mac Energy Addendum (Form 1004A) from 1989, the energy savings of $629 annually or $50 ($629/12 = $52.41) monthly at today's current interest rate of 3.6% for seven years results in the calculations shown in Exhibit 6.20.

Converting this $1,400 (calculated in Exhibit 6.20) into a percentage of the overall cost or sale price of the subject property provides a comparative unit of measure. For example, if the property being

Exhibit 6.20   Energy Savings Calculations

HP-12C Calculations for DCF of Energy Savings	Sample Support for Input
f clear FIN	This clears the calculator
7 g n Payments are based on monthly savings. Therefore, pressing the blue g key prior to pressing n shows 84 months or payments (7 years × 12 months per year).	7 years is based on Fannie Mae/Freddie Mac instructions from the old Energy Addendum (Form 1004A)
3.6% i	Based on the current mortgage rate as per Fannie Mae/Freddie Mac Form 1004A
$52.14 in monthly utility savings PMT	Energy savings based on HERS rater report (Exhibit 6.19)
PV	Results in $1,374, rounded to $1,400
Present value of energy savings: $1,400	

appraised is under contract at $150,000, the adjustment is only 0.9% of the overall sale price ($1,400/$150,000). This is a minor adjustment and well within the line-item guidelines of the secondary mortgage market. However, an across-the-board adjustment is not appropriate. Each sale must be measured against the subject property in order to develop an appropriate adjustment with support and explanation. The biggest challenge for appraisers is finding sufficient details about the comparable sales to understand how their energy efficiency compares to the appraisal property. Improving the accuracy of the MLS and opening the RESNET HERS database would greatly improve this process and result in more credible value opinions.

As a test of reasonableness for this example, a comparison of this indication to a paired sale or cost difference provides three sources to lend credibility to the adjustment. If credible paired sales reveal that the market does not pay more, the mathematical calculations are fruitless.

The HERS Index scale shown in Exhibit 6.21 reveals that a standard new home has an index rating of 100 and the subject property, located in southern New Mexico, has an index rating of 58. The subject is 42% more energy efficient than the standard new home based on this scale (standard new code-built home HERS Index less subject's HERS Index). The energy costs of the 1,800-sq.-ft. conditioned space are estimated at approximately $1,237.60 per year, or $103.13 per month based on the following report.

Exhibit 6.21   Comparison of HERS Index Ratings

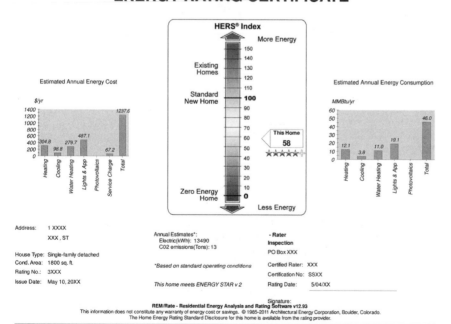

HOME PERFORMANCE WITH ENERGY STAR
ENERGY RATING CERTIFICATE

Section B5-3.3 of the 2013 Fannie Mae *Selling Guide* references the HERS Index and requires that the index rating on existing homes with energy-efficient improvements be included in the mortgage transaction. Below is an excerpt from the 2013 *Selling Guide*:

Energy Report Requirements

A Home Energy Rating Systems (HERS) energy rater must prepare a written energy report. A HERS rater is accredited under the Mortgage Industry National Home Energy Rating Standards (HERS Standards), as adopted by the Residential Energy Services Network (RESNET®).

The energy report must:

- identify the recommended energy improvements and expected costs of the completed improvements;
- specify the monthly energy savings to the borrower; and
- verify that the recommended energy improvements are cost-effective. Energy improvements are determined to be cost-effective when the cost of the improvements, including maintenance, is less than the present value of the energy saved over the useful life of the improvements.[17]

Utility Costs

Utility costs for existing homes should be available from the property owner. A review of utility costs over the last 12 months may be used to develop the average monthly costs. However, the electric and gas bills or other heating expenses should be reviewed, and the occupants

---

THE *HERS* INDEX REPORT AND THE ADDENDUM FORM

The HERS Index report provides the following features requested on the addendum as verified by a rater:

- HERS Index rating and number of stars awarded on rating certificate
- Date certified
- Certifier
- Estimated energy costs and energy savings
- Conditioned square footage of house
- Number of bedrooms
- Size of water heater
- Window type
- Wall R-value
- Blower door test and rate
- Envelope tightness rating
- Slab type

This list reveals how important it is for appraisers to attach the HERS Index report in its entirety to the addendum. The report provides support for the description applied in the appraisal report. Because appraisers are not energy raters, completing the addendum form without this type of report is impossible for most.

---

17. *Selling Guide: Fannie Mae Single Family*, Fannie Mae (October 22, 2013), 745. The most current version of the *Selling Guide* can be found at www.fanniemae.com/singlefamily/originating-underwriting.

should be interviewed to ensure that the bills are relevant. The lifestyle of the occupant or occupants makes a major difference in utility costs. The tracking of actual energy costs compared to estimates by various energy models has proven modeling programs to be reasonably accurate, except for unusual circumstances that are usually the result of occupant behavior. The inclusion of average monthly energy costs in the addendum is not a guarantee that the costs will be the same for the next owners. The first portion of the addendum explicitly addresses that the form is not a warranty or guarantee of any particular outcome.

Energy Audit

The next portion of the energy-efficient items section of the addendum form accommodates an energy audit that may have been performed on the house. If the energy audit upgrades were made, they should be listed in the comments section as part of the documentation of the physical characteristics of the appraised property. Ask the owner if the improvements made a difference in the actual utility costs, and document the findings on the addendum along with the source of the information. The difference in utility costs before and after the energy upgrades provides factual data for the appraiser's analysis.

An infrared photograph of the subject property can be a useful attachment to the addendum. Infrared photography quickly displays the leakage from the building envelope that is not tightly sealed. An infrared camera is designed for high-performance thermal imaging and measurements. The camera looks similar to any other camera, but it detects infrared energy and converts it into an electronic signal. From the electronic signal, a thermal image can perform temperature calculations.

CAUTION IS NEEDED WHEN USING ELECTRIC BILLS TO MEASURE ENERGY EFFICIENCY

Energy conservation is not the same as energy efficiency. The following factors should be considered when analyzing actual electric bills:

· The typical thermostat setting in different seasons

· The maintenance program of the HVAC system

· How often the furnace and air conditioner are serviced
 (Service should occur at least annually, but every six months is preferable.)

· How often the furnace filter is changed
 (HVAC contractors suggest that the filter be changed monthly.)

· Any unusual plug loads that may affect energy costs

· The use of any electrical items, such as floor fans, a kiln for ceramic firing, or gaming and entertainment equipment that can create higher-than-average plug loads

· Occupancy
 (For example, is the house occupied less than 12 months out of the year?)

Be sure to question the occupants about these factors to gain a better sense of the electric bill's reliability as a measure of the structure's energy efficiency. Based on consideration of the above factors, appraisers can make informed decisions about how reliable actual energy bills may be in judging the structure's energy use.

In 2012, the Florida Power and Lights utility company reported the following as the top five home energy users for its service area:

1. Air conditioner

2. Pool pump

3. Water heater

4. Lighting

5. Clothes dryer

These items deserve emphasis when updating existing homes to maximize energy efficiency in this type of climate. For new homes, energy-efficient products and possible ways to integrate mechanicals to maximize efficiencies for these top five energy uses should be researched. Some equipment may cost more up front, but overall costs may be less considering the payback in energy saved. This type of product study is similar to a cost-benefit analysis more often provided on high-performance commercial buildings.

These top energy uses often explain why some energy estimates are higher than the actual energy bills. In a particular subject property, one or more of these systems may not be properly equipped for energy efficiency, may need repair or replacement, or may be overused by the occupants. Utility companies in many areas provide lists of the top energy users in their areas. A list for your climate zone may be much different than the list for this hot and humid climate. This type of information is helpful for real estate professionals and buyers to consider in viewing and judging energy efficiency.

Infrared photographs of two different houses are shown in Exhibit 6.22. Which house will draw a buyer more quickly and possibly with a premium? The house pictured on the left shows signs of poorly installed or failing insulation, leaking windows, and air leakage around the light fixtures. This photograph was taken from the outside of the house on a cold day. The areas with darker shading indicate that the insulation is keeping the heat in the interior conditioned space from escaping through the exterior walls. Places where interior heat is escaping to the exterior are indicated by lighter shading. The photograph of the house on the right shows a tightly sealed house with only a couple of small areas where heat loss is occurring.

Knowledge of the infrared camera's use is an important skill that most appraisers, builders, and sales agents do not have. Therefore, any infrared photographs used in a report should be from a trained professional who can validate the proper use of the camera and photograph results.

A free online tool, Home Energy Saver Pro (http://hespro.lbl.gov), provides tips on saving energy and estimating annual energy costs in a given house. Once details about the home's construction are provided, the tool provides an estimate of annual energy costs and suggests upgrades. The more accurate and detailed the input, the more accurate the estimate. However, this type of energy audit should not be addressed on the addendum form because it is not a certified or formal audit.

HELPFUL HINT FOR NONAPPRAISERS

Providing infrared photographs in MLS photo galleries would be a good marketing tool for energy-efficient homes and may help promote public awareness of energy efficiency.

Exhibit 6.22   Infrared Photographs

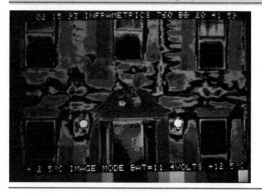 

Source: Photographs appear courtesy of the EPA.

Comments

The comments box at the bottom of the second page of the addendum form provides the chance to describe additional energy-efficient
features that are not specifically listed on the page. Space is provided
to quote sources for the data presented and discuss any operational
problems that may be known or not understood. Appraisers may
need to apply an extraordinary assumption regarding the reports or
data received.

Exhibit 6.23 shows the energy-efficient items section of the form
completed for a hypothetical property. The information provided here
is for educational purposes only and is not from an actual property.
Note that the comments section provides sufficient space to address
features that are not included elsewhere on the page or new items
that may develop in this ever-changing field.

As of the publication of this book, the Energy Star certification
system is at Version 3. An ES Certificate should provide the version and
date rated. When comparing ES-rated houses of the same age, the ES
version will most likely be the same. However, if an appraiser must use
comparable sales that have a two-year difference or more in age, different ES versions may come into play.

Most databases do not provide the ES version. However, this
information does not usually present a valuation issue unless comparisons are made between houses rated under different versions.
Obtaining the ES version for comparable sales will be next to impossible unless databases begin to populate this data field. The Real
Estate Transaction Standard is creating progress with standard green
fields, but MLS systems are slow to adopt. If appraisers cannot find
the ES version information for comparable sales, they must consider
whether the buyer factored in the version differences in the buying
decision. If buyers do not see this as a value-determining factor, then
an adjustment would not be supportable.

Exhibit 6.23   Sample Completed Energy-Efficient Items Section of the Addendum Form

ENERGY EFFICIENT ITEMS

The following items are considered within the appraised value of the subject property:

Insulation	☐ Fiberglass Blown-In ☒ Foam Insulation ☐ Cellulose ☐ Fiberglass Batt Insulation ☐ Other (Describe): ☐ Basement Insulation (Describe): ☒ HERS Insulation Installed Rating: ☒ 1 ☐ 2 ☐ 3 (See Glossary)	R-Value: ☒ Walls R-19 ☒ Ceiling R-38 ☐ Floor
Envelope	Envelope Tightness: Unit: ☐ CFM25 ☐ CFM50 ☒ ACH50 ☐ ACHnatural ☒ Envelope Tightness based on Blower Door Test	
Water Efficiency	☐ Reclaimed Water System (Explain): ☒ Cistern - Size: 5,000 Gallons ☒ Greywater reuse system ☐ WaterSense® fixtures ☐ Rain Barrels Provide Irrigation	Location of cistern: Rear yard
Windows	☒ ENERGY STAR® ☒ Low E ☐ High Impact ☐ Storm ☒ Double Pane ☐ Triple Pane ☐ Tinted ☐ Solar Shades	
Day Lighting	☐ Skylights - #: ☒ Solar Tubes - #: 2 ☐ Other (Explain):	☒ ENERGY STAR Light Fixtures
Appliances	ENERGY STAR® Appliances: ☒ Dishwasher ☒ Refrigerator ☐ Other:	Water Heater: ☒ Solar ☐ Heat Pump ☐ Tankless ☐ Coil Size: Gal.	Appliance Energy Source: ☐ Propane ☒ Electric ☐ Natural Gas ☐ Other (Describe):
HVAC (Describe in Comments Area)	☒ High Efficiency HVAC SEER: Efficiency Rating: 98 % AFUE* % *Annual Fuel-Utilization Efficiency	☐ Heat Pump Efficiency Rating: COP: HSPF: SEER: EER:	☐ Thermostat/Controllers	☐ Passive Solar (Defined in Glossary)
	☒ Programmable Thermostat		☐ Radiant Floor Heat	☐ Geothermal
Energy Rating	☒ ENERGY STAR ®Home - Version: 2 ☐ Other (Describe): Home Energy Score (HES) (Score range 1-10): ☐ Certification Attached	
Indoor Air Quality	☐ Indoor Air PLUS Package	☐ Energy Recovery Ventilator Unit or Whole Building Ventilation System	☒ Non Toxic Pest Control
HERS Information	Rating: 60	Monthly Energy Savings on Rating: $98	Date Rated: 7/2010
Utility Costs	Average Annual Utility Cost: $ 1,500 per month based on: bill review		# of Occupants: 4
Energy Audit	☐ Infrared Photograph Attached Has an energy audit/rating been performed on the subject property? ☐ Yes ☒ No ☐ Unknown If yes, comment on work completed as result of audit.		

Comments (Include source for information provided in this section)	Information was provided by:
	Owner provided the appraiser with a specification list, blueprints, and worksheet from the third party rater. The owner reports no changes have been made since the house was built in 2010. The actual utility bill is within 7% of the estimate provided by the HERS Index report based on plans and specifications.
Attach documents or reference them in your workfile	The envelope tightness is 2 ACH50 and indicates a tighter seal than the current building code requirement. The Icynene Insulation provides additional soundproofing, envelope sealing, and good insulation factors. The cost is slightly higher than fiberglass batt insulation but is rapidly renewable material using a bio-based material and it will not shrink over time as batt insulation may.
The energy element is the most measurable element of green or high performance housing.	The cistern provides irrigation for landscaping. Water is expensive in this market; therefore, cisterns are a premium in this market. The property has public water for potable use. (See fire hydrant in photo) ENERGY STAR®: http://www.energystar.gov/index.cfm?c=bldrs_lenders_raters.nh_2011_comments

Solar Panels Section

The solar panels section (page 3) of the addendum form works in harmony with PV Value online software used to estimate the value of the energy produced by solar photovoltaic (PV) systems. This section of the form can be a great guide for sales agents, builders, or appraisers to ensure that the appropriate data is gathered to allow for a more accurate valuation of the PV system. The details of a solar PV system should be in the paperwork provided by the installer. Ask the homeowner to have these documents ready when you call to make the appointment. If the paperwork has been lost, a call to the installer may result in the information needed to develop a value. Ideally, the installer would complete this section of the addendum form at the time of purchase and the homeowner will keep this crucial information. It would be ideal if it became standard practice within the solar PV installation industry to label electric boxes with the applicable data found in the addendum.

> **HELPFUL HINT FOR NONAPPRAISERS**
>
> After the examination of the energy-efficient items section of the addendum form in this chapter, it should be easy for a homeowner to see why the addendum and its documentation should be kept with the transfer of the house. Details of construction are easily forgotten, yet they can be extremely important in the future resale or valuation of a home. Public record does not document sufficient detail to complete this addendum. As changes such as updates or additions to a structure occur, homeowners should also update the addendum as an ongoing record for many future uses, such as refinance, sale, or maintenance.

The likelihood that a residential appraiser will encounter a property with a solar PV system or solar thermal water heater is increasing, based on the *US Solar Market Trends 2012* report. Almost 95,000 grid-connected PV installations were completed in 2012, representing a 46% increase over the number of installations in 2011. Residential systems accounted for 90% of these installations. Residential installations of solar PV systems grew by 60% in 2012 over 2011. At the end of 2012, 316,000 PV installations were connected to the US grid, including 283,000 residential installations. The report indicates that the top 10 states for 2012 installations are California, Arizona, New Jersey, Nevada, Massachusetts, North Carolina, Hawaii, Colorado, Maryland, and New York. The top 10 states change yearly, mainly due to the incentives offered, mandates, or changes in utility rates.[18] Appraisers and sales agents who begin learning about solar systems prior to encountering them in the field will be prepared to more confidently develop value opinions and provide better marketing.

Much of the terminology used in this section of the addendum form is explained in the *PV Value User Manual*. The manual and value tool are free downloads available from Sandia National Laboratories at http://energy.sandia.gov. Anyone using this software should read the manual and understand the methodology used.

Appraisers must follow the relevant portions of USPAP when using DCF analysis.[19] Statement 2 of USPAP addresses DCF analysis and cautions appraisers to make sure that controlling inputs are consistent with market evidence and prevailing market attitudes. The PV Value tool allows appraisers to change various inputs to reflect their local market trends. Appraisers should explain the basis for the inputs used to allow clients to understand the forecasts.

Residential appraisers should have a good understanding of the discounted cash flow and have credible support for the inputs. The PC Value tool is easy to use and similar to Excel spreadsheet models that many appraisers use.

To provide readers of an appraisal report with confidence in the DCF model for valuing a solar PV system, some test of reasonableness should be considered. The best test of reasonableness is a comparison of the results of the DCF model to paired sales and cost less all forms of depreciation (i.e., losses in value due to physical, functional, or external economic causes) or loss. If the DCF model consistently mirrors a similar value indication as other methods, it can be used with confidence in your market.

The *PV Value User Manual* provides an explanation of the valuation method for the income capitalization approach as follows:

> The method of valuation for the income approach uses the present value of the future energy production…This is accomplished using the following formula for each year over the remaining life of the project:
>
> $$((E_{kWh} * Deg_{rate} * U_{rate} * UEsc_{rate} * Disc_{rate}) - O\&M_{yr16} * Discrate$$
>
> E_{kWH} = Annual energy output (kWh)
>
> Deg_{rate} = Module degradation rate (%)
>
> U_{rate} = Current utility rate (¢/kWh)
>
> $UEsc_{rate}$ = Utility escalation rate (%)
>
> $Disc_{rate}$ = Discount rate (%)
>
> $O\&M_{yr16}$ = O&M expenses for year 16 (¢)
>
> The degradation rate is calculated starting in the first year, the utility rate escalation % and the discount rate are calculated starting the first month of year 2, and the O&M expenses are calculated for year 16 only.

---

18. Larry Sherwood, *US Solar Market Trends 2012* (Boulder City, Nevada: Interstate Renewable Energy Council, 2013), 5.

19. *Uniform Standards of Professional Appraisal Practice*, 2014-2015 ed., U-19.

If the appraisal is made in year 15 and beyond, an option comes up asking the user whether the inverter has been replaced. If it has been replaced before the 15-year warranty period, the appraisal range of value estimate will be higher. If it has not been replaced within the 15-year warranty period, the O&M amount will then be discounted for the remaining warranty lifetime of the panels, which will result in a lower appraisal range of value estimate.[20]

Some lenders require appraisers to provide the formulas used in DCF models. When a lender will not accept the explanation of the methodology explained above, an alternative is to build a DCF using Excel. A sample of a DCF using the PV Value software and using Excel will be provided later in this chapter.

Resource for Utility Cost per Kilowatt-Hour

The cost per kilowatt-hour (kWh) can be obtained from the local utility company. When the Green Button initiative is implemented, it will be a good resource for homeowners to quickly and accurately download their utility usages and kWh charges. The PV Value software is considered to be fairly accurate at determining the cost per kWh. Another source for obtaining utility costs per kWh in a given area is OpenEI's Utilities Gateway at http://en.openei.org/wiki/Gateway:Utilities.

If information on the solar PV system cannot be obtained to complete the addendum form, it may be next to impossible to develop a credible value opinion, even with paired sales data. It is difficult to pair sales when you have insufficient knowledge of the property's important features. If the solar PV features were unknown for a pair of sales that are otherwise similar, the results of this analysis would not be credible.

Leased Versus Owned Solar PV Systems

Whether a solar PV system is leased or owned by a homeowner is a vital piece of information that must be correctly identified by appraisers and listing agents. The 61% growth in residential solar PV installations in 2012 compared to 2011 is fueled by the increasing use of leases and

---

THE GREEN BUTTON INITIATIVE

The website www.greenbuttondata.org provides users with access to their residential or commercial building's energy usage rates. The Green Button initiative was launched in 2012 to encourage utility companies to provide their customers with access to information about their utility use. Once the initiative is implemented, users will be able to access the energy usage rates for the residential or commercial building. While many utility companies have supported or pledged to support this program, none have implemented it as of yet.

Once the program gets underway, homeowners should be able to download their energy use information into an Excel spreadsheet or other type of software. Confidential user data will be kept private and password protected. This tool can assist energy users in understanding their energy loads and patterns, which may help occupants in lowering their energy use. Users can also transfer data to a third-party service for analysis. An energy auditor or agent might use this data to report actual energy use prior to a sale. If this data sharing standard is implemented in your area, it may be useful in estimating energy use on properties you appraise.

---

20. Jamie L. Johnson and Geoffrey T. Klise, *PV Value® User Manual v. 1.1* (Sandia National Laboratories, Energy Sense Finance, and the US Department of Energy, 2012), 9.

third-party ownership of these systems.[21] The leased or third-party ownership is usually identified as personal property and subject to personal property tax. Personal property value should not be included in the real property value without clearly identifying how much is attributed to personal property. Appraisers should notify the lender if a system is not owned and obtain specific direction from the lender on how they may want to proceed. The secondary mortgage market (Fannie Mae and Freddie Mac), the US Department of Veterans Affairs, and the US Department of Housing and Urban Development arc expected to provide updated guidelines on solar PV systems to clarify their position on leased systems. The current guidelines indicate that personal property should not be included in real property value.

The terms of the lease or third-party ownership are important factors that may affect the property's marketability. Factors to consider include the following:

- Some leases cannot be paid off during the first six years due to the tax depreciation implications for the leasing companies. If that is the case, how does that affect the marketability of the property? Some buyers may not be wiling to purchase a house with a leased system.
- The solar PV system remains in the name and ownership of the leasing company rather than the property owner.
- Some leases are paid in full up front, while others are paid monthly with a specified buy-out agreement.
- Some leasing companies charge a monthly maintenance fee.
- Most leases identify the solar PV system as personal property and require the property owner to pay personal property taxes.
- In the event that the roof needs replacing, the property owner is often responsible for the cost to remove and replace the solar PV system.
- Some leases allow a new buyer to assume the lease if the buyer's credit rating is acceptable to the leasing company. This can delay the closing of a sale transaction.

A problem in valuing a property with a solar PV system is that the system may be assumed to be owned when it is actually leased. Suppose a house with a solar PV system sold. The purchase required a mortgage. The mortgagee's appraisal and MLS listing on the property reflect an owned solar PV system. The buyer closes on the deal and a short time later receives the payment information on the *leased* solar PV system. All parties involved except the leasing company and seller were shocked to learn of the error, which was multiplied by various parties making assumptions. Assuming that a system is owned is dangerous and usually results in an errors and omissions claim or court battle that neither the appraiser nor the agent want to experience.

If a listing agent and appraiser used the solar panels section of

---

21. Sherwood, *US Solar Market Trends*, 2.

the addendum, it would lead them through the information they need from the owner. If you encounter a leased system, request that a copy of the lease be provided to all parties, including the lender. The terms of the lease may be detrimental to the mortgagee and could materially affect the transaction. The lender may be wise in seeking a legal opinion on the lease terms and how they might affect the mortgage. Several questions may arise in this type of situation, as shown in Exhibit 6.24.

Some solar PV systems are purchased using Property Assessed Clean Energy (PACE) financing, which is designed to encourage the installation of renewable energy systems and improve energy efficiency by helping property owners overcome the barrier of high up-front costs for energy equipment and installation. A PACE loan is more properly called a *lien* because the loan is attached to the taxes as a special assessment. Therefore, it often trumps the first mortgage. Secondary mortgage markets usually refuse to make loans on properties with PACE loans. Some newer PACE loan programs have been developed that would not trump the first mortgage position. Therefore, the appraiser should research the PACE loan type before making such claims.

A leased solar PV system may lower the electric bill. Making this determination requires a review of the electrical bill compared to the monthly lease costs.

Exhibit 6.24	Solar PV Systems: Questions and Answers
Question:	Suppose that you make a site visit to a property with a solar PV system. During the process of inquiring about the system, the owners reported that they got a great deal on it. They received a PACE loan at 1% with payments over 20 years made through the tax bill. You discover that this PACE loan trumps the first mortgage position. Should the appraiser notify the lender or proceed with the appraisal and let the lender deal with the problem? If you notify the lender, the assignment might be canceled.
Answer:	Honesty and integrity are characteristics that should be synonymous with the appraisal profession. Notify the lender, and allow the lender to make a decision about proceeding with the appraisal or canceling the assignment. The appraiser may only receive a fee for the site visit upon cancellation, but he or she will maintain honesty and integrity, which is invaluable. The appraiser should discuss the source of information provided as well as any operational problems known or suspected and how they might affect the valuation in the comments section at the bottom of the solar panels page of the addendum form. If other sources of renewable energy such as wind, hydropower, or biomass are used, provide the details of the source in sufficient detail to support the analysis.
Question:	If a solar PV system is leased, does the lease have value?
Answer:	The value of the lease depends on the energy produced compared to the cost of the lease and the local market. The appraiser should take the following steps: · Analyze the lease for terms that might affect the transfer or potential added value or premium to the sale price of the real estate. · Review market data to develop a supported opinion of the effect the solar PV system had on the sale price. · Determine if there are sufficient sales in the market to develop a paired sales analysis of a sale with a leased solar PV system compared to a similar property without a solar PV system. The appraiser should carefully analyze the above-mentioned factors and support the conclusion in the report. It would be wrong to avoid analyzing or disclosing the lease. If the lease system is considered personal property and influenced the sale price, it should be considered a concession that must be disclosed. It is possible that the existence of a leased solar PV system negatively affected the sale price.

Power purchase agreements (PPAs) are similar to solar PV system leases. The property owner is referenced as a host for the system. The PPA retains full ownership of the solar PV system and leases the rooftop of the property for a nominal amount, $1.00 per year. The host or property owner agrees to purchase 100% or the electricity produced by the solar PV system for a specified period (usually 20 years). This type of agreement poses the same issues as solar PV leases. It is uncertain how the secondary mortgage market will view PPAs in their guidelines.

Although the most current edition (version 1.2) of the Real Estate Standards Organization (RESO) *Data Dictionary* includes green search fields for solar PV size and ownership type, not all MLS systems have implemented such a field. However, the MLS for Phoenix (Arizona) recently added "Solar PV Size" as a searchable field. Most listings do not provide information on the age of the PV system or the energy produced by it. Many inverters have digital meters that show the energy produced as of the current date. However, that number will change. Knowing the average energy production for the last three years of the system is helpful in understanding the actual production compared to the manufacturer's suggested production.

Solar Thermal Water Heating System

A solar thermal water heating system can be described on the same page of the addendum form as a solar PV system. However, solar PV systems produce electricity, while solar thermal water heating systems heat water. These two systems have dramatically different functions and costs. HUD requires a backup system for solar thermal water heating systems. The addendum form provides the details that HUD currently requires.

Exhibit 6.25 shows two photographs. The first is of a solar thermal panel, and the second is of a solar PV system that produces electricity. The functions and costs of these two systems are dramatically different.

Completing the Solar Panels Section

An example of a filled-out solar panels section of the addendum form is shown in Exhibit 6.26. This completed section of the form provides all the inputs necessary to complete a DCF analysis on the solar PV system. The fields in the addendum form were developed based on the input for the PV Value software tool. Exhibit 6.27 shows the value developed using the PV Value tool accompanied by a sample explanation of the DCF inputs required to allow the client to understand the premise of this method.

In this appraisal problem, the information found on the addendum form provides the needed details about the system and the data source. The discount rate applied is based on the typical property owner's consideration of alternative investments or the purchaser's weighted average cost of capital. The basis points represent the risk premium that a prudent investor would consider. The interest rate is based on a Fannie Mae 30-year, fixed-rate mortgage. The purchaser

Exhibit 6.25 Residential Solar Power Systems

A solar thermal water heating panel

A solar photovoltaic (PV) system that produces electricity

Exhibit 6.26 Sample Completed Solar Panels Section of the Addendum Form

Solar Panels

The following items are considered within the appraised value of the subject property:

Description	Array #1 ☐ Leased ☒ Owned	Array #2 ☐ Leased ☐ Owned	Description	Solar Thermal Water Heating System
kW (size)	9.12 kW		If Active System - type	☒ Direct ☐ Indirect
Manufacturer of Panels	Solar Power Industries, Inc.		If Passive System - type	☐ Integral collector ☐ Thermosyphon
Warranty on Panels	25 years		Storage Tank Size	# Gallons: 120
Age of Panels	3 years		Collector Type	☒ Flat-Plat Collector ☐ Integral Collector ☐ Evacuated-Tube Solar
Energy Production kWh per Array	11,300 kWh annually			

Source for Energy Production Estimate	Monitoring software for system—copy attached		**Back-Up System**	☒ Conventional Water Htr ☐ Tankless On Demand ☐ Tankless Heat Pump
Location (Roof, Ground, Etc.)	Roof		**Age of System**	3 years
Tilt/Slope for Array	18.5 degrees		**Warranty Term**	10
Azimuth per Array	180 degrees		**Manufacturer**	Energy Star
Age of Inverter(s)	3 years		**Solar Energy Factor (SEF)** (Rating range 1 to 11 - higher number is more efficient)	1.8
Manufacturer	Xantrex			
Warranty Term	10 years			

Name of Utility Company: Austin Energy	Cost per kWh charged by Company: $0.10829/kWh
Comments (Discuss incentives available for new panels, condition of current panels, and any maintenance issues. If leased, provide the lease terms.) A free online tool and manual for valuing the energy production of the Solar PV System is available at www.pvvalue.com Download the PV Value™ Manual for explanation of the solar terms on this form and inputs used in the PV Value Tool.	Discuss source of information and define other renewable energy sources, such as wind, hydropower, biomass power, etc. This five-unit multifamily property has a three-year old solar PV system that is monitored. The owner provided the monitoring report showing the actual production reported at an average of 11,300 kWh annually. The owner provided the solar thermal water heating system information based on the documentation from the installer. The owner reports no maintenance problems since its installation. After installation, the utility bill for this property was reduced by $50 per month. The energy produced by the Solar PV System will be valued using the PV Value Tool and a paired sale analysis.

Exhibit 6.27 PV Value Solution to 9.1 kW Solar PV System

Energy Sense Finance | **Sandia National Laboratories** | **PV Value™   Photovoltaic Energy Valuation Model v. 1.1**

Choose Property Type: ○ Residential   ● Commercial   [Office / Warehouse / Shopping Center / Multi-Use]

Solar Resource Calculation	
Zip Code	78757
System Size in Watts	9,210
Derate Factor	0.770
Commissioning report is required to override default derate factor	
Commissioning Report #	
Module Degradation Rate	0.5
Array Type *Fixed*	
Array Tilt (unchecked = latitude) □	0.0
Array Azimuth (default = South)	180
Click to Calculate PV Production	kWh Produced/Year 11,482

Discount Rate Calculation	
Basis Points (low)	50
Basis Points (high)	200
Basis Points (average)	125
Custom Rate	5.00
Discount Rate (low)	5.50
Discount Rate (average)	6.25
Discount Rate (high)	7.00

Electricity Rate Inputs	
Click to Update Utility Specific Electricity Rate	Austin Energy-TXU Energy Real Co / LP
Commercial Rate ¢/kWh	10.829
□ User Defined (check box) ¢/kWh	
Utility Escalation Rates for	TX
Commercial Escalation Rate -EIA	1.73
□ User Defined (check box)	

Operation & Maintenance Inputs	
15-Year O&M Expenses as a function of the system size	
O&M Expenses ¢/W	56
□ User Defined (check box) ¢/W	
Est. Inverter Replacement Cost $	2,447.23

System Age and Remaining Lifetime	
Module Warranty/Years	25
Age of System/Years	3
Remaining Energy/Years	22
Is this a Lease to Purchase option? □	Check for Buyout Valuation

Appraisal Range of Value Estimate	
Low	$ 13,432.17
Average	$ 14,403.30
High	$ 15,475.13

Legend: User Input / User Input Override / Calculated Value

Explanation of PV Value Solution to 9.1 kW Solar PV System

The value of the solar PV system is based on an income capitalization method known as *discounting of the future energy produced*. The typical purchaser of residential property makes a buying decision for solar PV on the basis of the anticipated energy production. Instead of paying the utility company to provide electricity, the owner of a property with a solar PV system is producing a larger portion of electricity using solar power. The typical buyer may not be able to develop a discounted cash flow (DCF) analysis, but the individuals' thought process is income-oriented. As a result, it is logical for appraisers to consider the contributory value of the solar PV system based on a DCF. Secondary mortgage market guidelines allow for the income method, as illustrated by the 1989 Energy Addendum (Fannie Mae Form 1004A/Freddie Mac Form 70A). Although this form is no longer used, it was developed by the secondary market and illustrates the credibility of this method.

The DCF program used to value the solar PV system's energy production is a free Web-based program supported by the Appraisal Institute (as stated in their January 31, 2012 press release, "Appraisal Institute Announces Support for New Solar Valuation Tool." The spreadsheet (PV Value tool) was developed by Solar Power Electric (also known as Energy Sense Finance) and Sandia National Laboratories. The tool works within a Microsoft Excel spreadsheet in which the energy value is developed over the system's remaining life. The tool considers the calculations as follows:

· The *derate rate* is the normal loss experienced in the conversion of direct current to alternating current and based on a custom rate from a shading analysis provided by the property owner. Otherwise, the tool defaults to 0.77, which is the same as the PV Watts standard derate. PV Watts is an online performance calculator for grid-connected PV systems.

· The PV Value software estimates the future solar energy production using information from PV Watts, available through the National Renewable Energy Laboratory (http://rredc.nrel.gov/solar/calculators/PVWATTS/version1).

· The *module degradation rate* begins the first day of production and is based on research by the National Renewable Energy Laboratory to demonstrate that the energy output of higher-quality crystalline silicone modules degrade at rates of 0.1% to 0.9% per year, and for some thin-film modules the current rate of yearly degradation can be 1% or more.

· The utility rate escalation percentage and the discount rate are calculated beginning the first month of the second year. The escalation rate is based on data from the Energy Information Agency (www.eia.gov/electricity).

· The operations and maintenance expenses are calculated for Year 16 only.

If the appraisal is made in Year 15 and beyond, an option comes up asking the user whether the inverter has been replaced. If it has been replaced before the 15-year warranty period, the appraisal range of the value estimate will be higher. If it has not been replaced within the 15-year warranty period, the operations and maintenance amount will then be discounted for the remaining warranty lifetime of the panels, which will result in a lower estimated range of value.

is seeking a 30-year, fixed-rate mortgage in this appraisal problem. Therefore, the same term is considered in this method.

The indicated value range for this example found by using this tool is $13,432.17 to $15,475.37. This range is within the value indications found using the following Microsoft Excel spreadsheet DCF (Exhibit 6.28) and represents 38% of cost from a survey of local solar PV companies ($41,040 based on $4.50 per watt, calculated as follows: 9.12 kw × 1,000 = 9,120 watts × $4.50).

Exhibit 6.28   DCF for Solar PV Valuation

Assumptions

System rated capacity	9.21 kW DC
System age	36 months
Warranty	25 years
Historical production	33,900 kWh since inception
Average monthly production	942 kWh per mo.
Degradation (est.)	0.5% per year
Average electricity cost	$0.108 per kWh
Projected inflation (electricity)	1.7% per year
Loss factor (1)	5.0% per year

Analysis Year	Annual Electric Output (kWh)	Average Electricity Cost ($/kWh)	Avoided Electricity Cost per Yr.	Loss* Factor 5.0%	Net Benefit
1	11,300	$0.108	$1,220	($61)	$1,159
2	11,244	$0.110	$1,235	($62)	$1,174
3	11,187	$0.112	$1,250	($63)	$1,188
4	11,131	$0.114	$1,266	($63)	$1,202
5	11,076	$0.116	$1,281	($64)	$1,217
6	11,020	$0.118	$1,297	($65)	$1,232
7	10,965	$0.120	$1,313	($66)	$1,247
8	10,910	$0.122	$1,329	($66)	$1,262
9	10,856	$0.124	$1,345	($67)	$1,278
10	10,802	$0.126	$1,361	($68)	$1,293
11	10,748	$0.128	$1,378	($69)	$1,309
12	10,694	$0.130	$1,395	($70)	$1,325
13	10,640	$0.133	$1,412	($71)	$1,341
14	10,587	$0.135	$1,429	($71)	$1,358
15	10,534	$0.137	$1,446	($72)	$1,374
16	10,482	$0.140	$1,464	($73)	$1,391
17	10,429	$0.142	$1,482	($74)	$1,408
18	10,377	$0.145	$1,500	($75)	$1,425
19	10,325	$0.147	$1,518	($76)	$1,443
20	10,273	$0.150	$1,537	($77)	$1,460
21	10,222	$0.152	$1,556	($78)	$1,478
22	10,171	$0.155	$1,575	($79)	$1,496

Present value at	6.25%	Annual discount rate	$15,121
Rounded			$15,000
GBA (sq. ft.)			4,000
Contributory value per sq. ft.			$3.78
Implied capitalization rate (Year 1 income / PV)			8.07%

* Loss factor considers costs of monitoring, replacement of PV inverters, etc.

The Excel DCF requires the appraiser to research the electric rate for this property, the inflation rate, the loss factor, and the cost of inverter replacement, which is included in the loss factor. The PV Value software automatically researches these facts by going directly to websites when the zip code and solar PV specifics are entered. Appraisers can research the same websites as PV Value and develop their own inputs, but this takes additional time with each assignment.

Location-Site Section

The location-site section of the addendum form is where the site element characteristics should be documented. The Walk Score website, www.walkscore.com, provides actual scores for specific locations as well as distances to nearest services, linkages, and transportation. The Walk Score has a range of 1 to 100, with a score of 100 indicating that a property in a specific location is walkable to all services. Some MLS systems automatically populate the Walk Score field once the address is entered. The more walkable a property is to employment and services, the more likely the owner is to not need a car, which results in lower monthly travel expenses and a lower carbon footprint.

The Transit Score is a patent-pending measure of how well a location is served by public transit. Transit Scores range from 0 to 100 and address the location of public transportation in relation to a property in a specific location. A list of US cities with available Transit Scores can be found at www.walkscore.com/transit-score-methodology.shtml.

The comments box at the end of the location-site section of the addendum form can be used for describing items that are not already listed in this section, such as drainage ponds, environmental features, or solar access. A discussion of the structure's orientation is helpful in understanding and communicating the effect it may have on the building's energy consumption. An example of a completed location-site section of the addendum form is shown in Exhibit 6.30.

Incentives Section

The definition of *market value* and underwriting guidelines require appraisers to report incentives that may offset the cost of construction. The cost approach always uses the cost as of the effective date of value. (For example, the effective date of value for loan purposes is typically the date that the appraiser inspected the property.)

Exhibit 6.29	How the Walk Score Works
Walk Score	**Description**
90-100	Walker's Paradise
	Daily errands do not require a car.
70-89	Very Walkable
	Most errands can be accomplished on foot.
50-69	Somewhat Walkable
	Some amenities within walking distance.
25-49	Car-Dependent
	A few amenities within walking distance.
0-24	Car Dependent
	Almost all errands require a car.

Source: Walk Score, www.walkscore.com.

Exhibit 6.30   Sample Completed Location-Site Section of the Addendum Form

Location - Site					
The following items are considered within the appraised value of the subject property:					
Walk Score	Score: 71	Source: http://www.walkscore.com (Example: http://www.walkscore.com)			
Public Transportation	☒ Bus – Distance: 3 Blocks	☐ Train – Distance: Blocks		☐ Subway – Distance: Blocks	
Site	Orientation - front faces: ☐ East/West ☒ North/South	Landscaping: ☐ Water Efficient ☐ Natural			
Comments	Bus fare is $1.50 per day or an annual pass can be purchased for unlimited use at $225 annually. The Walk Score indicates the property is in close proximity to services. A Walk Score of 100 indicates all services are within walking distance. The structure faces the south with a 4' overhang covering the large windows that provide daylighting. A large Oak Tree provides shade in the summer and sheds its leaves in the winter to provide warmth from the sun. The east and west walls have low-E windows with 4' overhang to prevent additional heat from the morning and afternoon sun. The landscaping irrigation uses a 5,000-gallon cistern on site. A small herb garden is planted along the perimeter of the west side of the house.				

Therefore, knowledge of incentives that might offset cost is important. Because incentives typically do not pass to the next buyer, they are not a sales concession consideration in the sales comparison approach.

Information on incentives can be found on the DSIRE website (www.dsireusa.org) for existing homes and non-green homes. Resources that provide incentive information are valuable for all property types.

Appraisers are not required to report incentives received at the time the existing home was built but as of the effective date of value. Cost is always developed based on the effective date of value. Therefore, the incentives should be deducted from gross cost to arrive at net cost.

Incentives are not a sales comparison concession because they do not pass on to the next buyer and they do not inflate the price of the house. Sales comparison concessions are only applied when the house sold for more because of the seller-paid concessions or personal property included in the sale.

A sample completed incentives section of the addendum form is provided in Exhibit 6.31.

As an example of the usefulness of incentive research, suppose that a bank-owned property is under contract. Upon inspection, the appraiser finds that the air-conditioner has been removed. The air-conditioner was a 19-SEER unit and must be replaced by the purchaser based on the purchase agreement. The lender requests that the appraisal be made subject to a new 19-SEER air-conditioner being installed with a cost to cure included in the analysis. A search of the DSIRE website revealed that a $1,500 rebate was available for installation of a 19-SEER air-conditioner that offset the cost to cure. This information was invaluable to the lender and the purchaser.

Exhibit 6.31   Sample Completed Incentives Section of the Addendum Form

Incentives – Amount of Incentive and Terms	
The following items are considered within the appraised value of the subject property:	
Federal	None
State	None
Local	The utility company offers a $1,500 rebate on a solar thermal water heating system. This rebate is an offset to cost and applied in the cost approach of this report. The rebate is available until December 31.
Source (For example www.dsireusa.org)	www.dsireusa.org provided the rebate information and it was further verified by viewing the website of the utility company.
Comments Incentives offset cost and should be reported in the cost approach section of the report. Incentives are typically not a sales comparison approach concession since they do not transfer with the property.	No additional incentives are known based on the source quoted. The solar thermal water heating incentive is an offset to the gross cost applied in the cost approach.

"Completed by" Section

The name and title of the person who completed the addendum form should be typed or signed and dated at the bottom of the fourth page of the form, after the incentives section, as shown in Exhibit 6.32. The appraiser will not be able to complete all of the fields that might apply to a property unless he or she has a complete set of construction and modeling reports. It is rare that appraisers are given this much detail. Therefore, any of the following people may have more detail to accurately complete the addendum than an appraiser would have:

- Builders
- Energy modelers
- Engineers

Exhibit 6.32 "Completed by" Section of the Addendum Form

Completed by:_____ Title:_____ Date:_____

CAUTION IS NEEDED WHEN USING THE ADDENDUM FORM

Appraisers who receive a completed addendum form from another property have the responsibility to review the data and request the supporting documents mentioned in this chapter. Appraisers are not building scientists and do not have the necessary skills to complete or identify certain construction items. If you do not have reports to verify the information in a specific section of the form, you are strongly encouraged to leave that section blank. Insist on the reports that should be available from the builder or seller to document your data sources.

Underwriting guidelines require lenders to pass on energy reports and purchase agreements to the appraiser. However, because of the third-party ordering required by the 2010 Dodd-Frank Wall Street Reform and Consumer Protection Act, these documents often do not reach appraisers. Appraisers should be diligent in obtaining documents prior to completing the addendum report.

- Architects
- Homeowners
- Third-party certifiers (such as HERS Index raters)

Appraisers can insert the addendum in an appraisal report as submitted or revise it to address omitted items. Appraisers have the responsibility of reviewing a completed addendum submitted by others and either accepting it as is or completing one with corrected information.

Glossary and Resources Section

The glossary and resources section on the last page of the addendum form provides definitions and web addresses for sites that can be helpful for understanding and completing the form. The addendum was never intended to be a systematic guide for valuing green features. Instead, it addresses USPAP Standard 2, which requires appraisers to describe the physical, economic, and locational features of the subject property in the reporting process. It also meets the objectives stated at the bottom of page 1 of the form and discussed earlier in this chapter.

Using the Addendum and Supporting Documents

The proper use of the Residential Green and Energy Efficient Addendum is a step in the right direction for appraisers and other real estate professionals dealing with the growing and changing field of high-performance buildings. However, the effective use of the addendum form is not guaranteed simply by its availability. The education process is ongoing, as market participants learn more about the types of documents, including the addendum form, that are necessary to support conclusions about green buildings.

The following is an example of an experience I had with a lender lacking the knowledge of the documents needed for a credible appraisal of a high-performance home, which resulted in an underwriting delay. A lender of energy-efficient mortgages ordered an appraisal of a proposed construction project that had a preliminary green rating. Upon receiving the order and documents supplied by the lender, I realized that neither the preliminary rating and worksheets nor the preliminary HERS Index rating were included. I called the lender and was told to proceed without the documents. The lender said, "You have everything you need, now just give us the value." However, I insisted on the documents prior to completion of the appraisal. A call to the builder solved this problem.

Lenders have a learning curve in the area of high-performance property. Appraisers must take additional time to assist in educating them on why certain documents are necessary.

As an example of a competent use of the addendum form that was ignored, a builder recently sent me a copy of an appraisal that had been completed on a newly built house. The builder had completed the addendum and provided it to the bank and appraiser. However, when the borrower received a copy of the appraisal, neither the borrower nor the builder could find any descriptions of the addendum features. The addendum was not attached to the appraisal and not referenced.

The lender is required by law to provide the borrower with a copy of the appraisal at least three days prior to closing. This requirement allows the borrower to review the appraisal and raise questions when errors or omissions are found.

Even if the features identified on the addendum form do not have additional value in the appraiser's supported opinion, they should be properly described. Otherwise, it appears that the appraiser totally ignored these features. The appraiser may have in fact considered the features in the analysis, but the lack of description raises questions about the competency and credibility of the value opinion.

ADDITIONAL RESOURCES

US Department of Energy
Information on the Green Button initiative to provide building power usage information and a list of utility companies that support the project can be found at www.energy.gov/data/green-button.

Solar, heat pump, tankless on-demand, and tankless coil water heaters are described at www.energy.gov/energysaver/articles/solar-water-heaters.

Building Energy Codes Program
The Building Energy Codes Program website (www.energycodes.gov/status-state-energy-code-adoption) provides a map of US climate zones, recommended building envelope ratings based on the International Energy Conservation Code, and a map showing the different versions of the IEEC adopted in each state.

Database of State Incentives for Renewables and Efficiency
The DSIRE website (www.dsireusa.org) includes an online database of state incentives for renewable energy and efficiency and information about Property Assessed Clean Energy (PACE) financing in specific markets.

Home Energy Score

Information on the Home Technology Office's Home Energy Score program can be found at http://www1.eere.energy.gov/buildings/residential/hes_index.html.

National Renewable Energy Laboratory

Information on passive solar design can be found in the article "Passive Solar Design for the Home," published in February 2001 and available at www.nrel.gov/docs/fy01osti/27954.pdf.

Information on infrared thermal imaging equipment is available at www.nrel.gov/vehiclesandfuels/energystorage/lab_infrared.html.

Building Performance Institute (BPI)

The Building Performance Institute Standard 2101 (www.bpi.org/tools_downloads.aspx) provides information on building envelope ratings. The BPI standard can be used as a tool for explaining terms and testing results.

City of Seattle Office of Sustainability and Environment

The *Green Building Glossary* at www.seattle.gov/dpd/GreenBuilding/Resources/Greenbuildingglossary/default.asp provides definitions of green terms as well as case studies and research data from the Seattle area.

Energy Star

Information on Energy Star-certified homes can be found at www.energystar.gov/index.cfm?c=new_homes.hm_index.

Mortgage News Daily

This online news source at www.mortgagenewsdaily.com/data provides information on general residential housing, including mortgage rates, housing production, home prices, housing inventory, and homeownership data.

National Association of Home Builders (NAHB)

Information on the National Green Building Standards can be found at www.nahb.org/page.aspx/generic/sectionID=2510 or www.homeinnovation.com.

National Association of Realtors (NAR)

The NAR has their own *Green Building Glossary* at www.greenresourcecouncil.org/green-resources/green-building-glossary. Their Green MLS Tool Kit at www.greenthemls.org provides case studies on how greening the MLS has changed the market, green data entry examples, and numerous other resources to assist local MLS boards in improving their systems.

Real Estate Standards Organization (RESO)

The RESO *Data Dictionary* at www.reso.org/data-dictionary provides a list of searchable green data fields. The dictionary can assist appraisers in retrieving data more quickly by knowing and using the appropriate fields.

Residential Energy Services Network (RESNET)

Information on the HERS insulation installed rating system can be found at www.resnet.us/standards/Enhancements_to_National_Rating_Standards.pdf.

The Appraisers Research Foundation

The Appraiser's Guide to Identifying Green Building Features in Homes, 2012 update, by Kathy Price-Robinson can be downloaded for free at www.appraiserresearch.org/research-results/green-guide.html. This guide was written for appraisers but is useful for homeowners, builders, and agents.

US Environmental Protection Agency (EPA)

Information on the EPA's WaterSense product labeling program can be found at www.epa.gov/watersense/new_homes/homes_final.html.

US Green Building Council (USGBC)

Information on the USGBC's Leadership in Energy and Environmental Design (LEED) program can be found at www.usgbc.org/DisplayPage.aspx?CMSPageID=1988.

Appraiser Independence Requirements, Fannie Mae Mortgage Market References, and the Appeal Process

As discussed earlier in this book, appraisers face specific challenges when dealing with high-performance housing in markets that may not yet have developed the data structure and systems for widespread understanding and acceptance of the relative value of green features. The regulatory environment in which appraisers work is also evolving, and the repercussions of the shifting regulatory landscape are felt not only by appraisers in complex assignments involving high-performance homes but also by the parties who rely on appraisers' opinions.

For example, the Appraiser Independence Requirements developed by the GSEs, governmental agencies, and industry representatives affect appraisers directly and also affect how appraisers deal with their clients, such as who is entitled to see an appraisal report. Likewise, specific guidelines on appraisal practice for loans in Fannie Mae and Freddie Mac programs place certain restrictions on what is and is not acceptable. As mentioned previously, individual lenders are charged with ensuring that appraisals submitted to GSEs conform to GSE guidelines as well as professional standards. Appeals of appraisals are an unfortunate reality, and an appeal may be warranted in the case of an appraisal of a high-performance home that should not be considered credible.

Appraiser Independence Requirements

The Appraiser Independence Requirements (AIR) were developed by Fannie Mae, the Federal Housing Finance Agency (FHFA), Freddie Mac, and key industry participants to replace the Home Valuation Code of Conduct (HVCC). The requirements became effective in 2010. To date, FHA and VA have not adopted AIR. Some frequently asked questions about AIR are addressed in the accompanying sidebar.

Fannie Mae Mortgage Market Appraisal References

It is worth reviewing Fannie Mae guidelines on appraisal practices to understand the constraints appraisers are under when developing the appraised value.

Question: Who receives copies of the appraisal and when?

Answer: AIR requires the lender to provide the borrower with a copy of the appraisal immediately after completion or within three days prior to closing. The lender may provide the borrower with a revised copy of the appraisal at closing. The borrower may sign a waiver to relinquish the right to the copy three days prior to closing, but the lender must provide a copy of the appraisal at closing if this is the case.

Comment: Just because the borrowers are required to receive a copy of the appraisal does not mean that the borrower is the appraiser's client. Any questions from the borrower regarding the appraisal should be provided in writing to the lender. AIR protects the appraiser from being pressured or harassed. The appeal process will be discussed later in this chapter.

Question: Who may communicate with the appraiser?

Answer: Anyone who is not part of the loan production staff, who is not compensated on a commission basis upon successful completion of a loan closing, or who does not ultimately report to any officer of the lender not independent of the loan production staff or process may communicate with the appraiser. The appraiser may communicate with the builder, real estate agent, or homeowner.

Comment: It is clear that appraisers may communicate with the builder, real estate agent, or homeowner to gather facts regarding the appraisal assignment. These people can provide important documents to support facts that are important to the appraisal process and valuable information to assist the appraiser in understanding buyer and seller motivations as well as property characteristics.

Question: Who may provide comparable data to the appraiser?

Answer: The real estate agent, builder, or seller may provide data, including sales, to the appraiser. However, it is the appraiser's responsibility to verify the data with other sources. The appraiser is not obligated to use the data if it is not the most applicable.

Comment: Data provided to the loan officer at the time of the loan application often does not make it to the appraiser. Anyone having data for the appraiser should not only provide the information to the lender but should make an additional copy to give the appraiser at the time of the site visit. The documents necessary for high-performance properties are discussed within this text. Presenting these documents will assist the lender or appraisal management company in understanding the complexity of the property. Therefore, an appraiser who is competent in valuing high-performance properties should be selected. If the borrower does not alert the lender's loan officer that the property is high-performance when making the application, the lender will have no way of knowing that a special appraiser is needed.

Question: Does AIR prohibit a lender from ordering a second appraisal?

Answer: No. Section II of the AIR document only prohibits lenders from ordering a second appraisal when they are attempting to influence the outcome of the first appraisal and are "value shopping."

Comment: The practice of "value shopping" by ordering appraisals to obtain the "needed" value is prohibited. Lenders must use a portal to upload and document the ordering of all appraisals involved in a specific assignment. They must also document the valid reasons for ordering the second appraisal. Specific rules regarding the ordering of the second appraisal will be addressed under the appeal process later in this chapter.*

---

* *Appraiser Independence Requirements Frequently Asked Questions (FAQs)* (Fannie Mae, November 2010), www.orea.ca.gov/pdf/FNMA%20FAQs.pdf.

A review of unacceptable appraisal practices identified in the guidelines indicates the responsibility of the appraiser to develop supported opinions of value using market data. In a market with limited data, it takes a skilled appraiser to develop a credible value result using acceptable appraisal practices.

Examples of Unacceptable Appraisal Practices

The following examples of unacceptable appraisal practices are excerpted from Fannie Mae's 2013 Selling Guide:

- Development of and/or reporting an opinion of market value that is not supportable by market data or is misleading.
- Misrepresentation of the physical characteristics of the subject property, improvements, or comparable sales.
- Selection and use of inappropriate comparable sales.
- Failure to use comparable sales that are the most locationally and physically similar to the subject property.
- Failure to make adjustments when they are clearly indicated.
- Use of unsupported descriptive comments or drawing unsupported conclusions from subjective observations. These actions may have a discriminatory effect.
- Use of unsupported assumptions, interjections of personal opinion, or perceptions about factors in the valuation process. These actions may have a discriminatory effect, and may or may not affect the use and value of a property.[1]

These unacceptable practices may all apply to appraisals of high-performance properties. An appraiser with a lack of knowledge about high-performance properties could be in danger of performing one or more of these unacceptable practices. If an appraisal report indicates that one or more of these unacceptable practices were involved in the appraisal, this would be reason to discuss the issue with the lender or client.

The Cost Approach Is Not Acceptable as a Sole Indicator of Value

Fannie Mae's 2013 *Selling Guide* clearly states that appraisals that rely solely on the cost approach as an indicator of market value are not acceptable.[2] The cost approach may be used and is often necessary to produce credible assignment results. Which approaches to use is a decision the appraiser must make based on the property type and the available data. Standards Rule 1-4 of USPAP makes it clear that appraisers should use the approaches to value that are necessary to produce credible appraisal reports.

Builders work on a cost-plus basis and often have difficulty understanding an appraisal that is based on market data and cost data and that is limited by a variety of guidelines and standards.

Lender Disclosure of Information to the Appraiser

The lender must disclose to the appraiser any and all information about the subject property of which the lender is aware if that infor-

---

1. *Selling Guide: Fannie Mae Single Family* (Washington, D.C.: Fannie Mae, January 17, 2013), 513-514. The most current version of the *Selling Guide* can be found at www.fanniemae.com/singlefamily/originating-underwriting.
2. Ibid., 592.

mation could affect the marketability of the property or the appraiser's opinion of the property's market value.[3]

For example, the lender must provide the appraiser with all appropriate financing data and sales concessions for the subject property that will be, or have been, granted by anyone associated with the transaction. In addition, the lender must provide the appraiser with a copy of the completed, ratified sales contract and all addenda for the property that is to be appraised, therefore ensuring that the appraiser has been given the opportunity to consider the financing and concessions in the transaction and their effect on value.

The lender must inform the appraiser of additional pertinent information that is not included in the sales contract. If the sales contract is amended during the process, the lender must provide the updated contract to the appraiser. Additional information that the lender is required to provide to the appraiser includes the following:

- Settlement charges
- Loan fees or charges
- Discounts to the sale price
- Payment of condominium or planned unit development fees
- Interest rate buydowns
- Financing that is below market rate
- Credits or refunds of borrower expenses
- Absorption of monthly expenses
- Assignment of rent payments
- Non-realty items included in the transaction (which may include a leased solar PV system or power purchase agreement)
- Any information about environmental hazards that arc in or on the subject property or in the property's vicinity that was obtained from the borrower, real estate broker, or any other party to the transaction (This information will allow the appraiser to consider any influence the hazard may have on the value and marketability of the property.)

Fannie Mae makes it clear that lenders are required to provide certain documents to appraisers. Because lenders use third-party companies (i.e., appraisal management companies) to order appraisals, these documents are often not transferred to appraisers. In the case of high-performance properties, HERS Index reports and high-performance certification documents should be provided to appraisers. It is important for borrowers, builders, and agents to realize that these types of documents are often the only clues the appraisal management company (AMC) may have that the property is complex and requires an appraiser who has the skills to meet the competency requirement and produce a credible appraisal report.

---

3.   Ibid., 516.

Energy-Efficient Mortgage Programs

Appraisers should become familiar with energy-efficient mortgages (EEMs) and the applicable lender guidelines. If the SAVE Act passes or the market continues to show a preference for energy-efficient homes, the market should begin to see more energy upgrades in new and existing homes. Reviewing MLS comment sheets for descriptions of energy upgrades in particular neighborhoods reveals trends that buyers are seeking. The highest and best use of an existing home that is not energy efficient may be "as improved with energy upgrades" if market analysis supports the trend.

Fannie Mae Requirements for the Energy Improvement Feature on Existing Construction

According to the 2013 Fannie Mae *Selling Guide*, a mortgage can be delivered before the energy improvements are completed if the lender represents and warrants that the postponed improvements will be completed within 180 days of the date of the mortgage note.[4] The guidelines indicate that the cost of the improvements must not represent more than 10% of the "as completed" appraised value of the property.

FHA Energy-Efficient Mortgages

The mortgage loan amount for an FHA energy-efficient mortgage can be increased by the cost of effective energy improvements. The maximum amount of the portion of the EEM for energy-efficient improvements is the lesser of 5% of

- the value of the property
- 115% of the median area price of a single-family dwelling, or
- 150% of the conforming Freddie Mac limit.

VA Energy-Efficient Mortgages

The VA energy-efficient mortgage caps the cost of energy improvements at $3,000 to $6,000. The amount of the increase must be supported by an increased valuation in an equal amount.

According to Chapter 7 of the *Lender's Handbook* (*VA Pamphlet 26-7*), acceptable energy-efficient improvements include, but are not limited to, the following:

- Solar heating systems, including solar systems for heating water for domestic use
- Solar cooling systems
- Caulking and weather stripping
- Furnace efficiency modifications limited to replacement burners, boilers, or furnaces designed to reduce the firing rate or achieve a reduction in the amount of fuel consumed as a result of increased combustion efficiency, devices for modifying flue openings that

---

4. Ibid., 531.

will increase the efficiency of the heating system, and electrical or mechanical furnace ignition systems that replace standing gas pilot lights

- Clock thermostats
- New or additional ceiling, attic, wall, and floor insulation
- Water heater insulation
- Storm windows or doors, including thermal windows or doors
- Heat pumps
- Vapor barriers[5]

Fannie Mae's Announcement on Energy Improvement Features

In 2010, Fannie Mae issued *Announcement SEL-2010-15: New Energy Improvement Feature and Other Related Updates,* which discusses their lender and appraiser requirements for energy-efficient mortgages. These requirements include the following:

- The lender is responsible for ensuring that the appraiser has been provided with a copy of the energy report.
- The lender is required to order an appraisal based on an interior and exterior property inspection during the site visit.
- The appraiser must determine the "as completed" value of the property subject to the energy improvements being completed.
- The lender is responsible for managing the improvement funds and for monitoring the completion of the energy-improvement work.
- The lender must obtain a certification of completion, and it must
  - Be completed by the appraiser,
  - State that the improvements were completed in accordance with the requirements and conditions in the original appraisal report, and
  - Include photographs of the completed improvements

Energy-efficient mortgages may be delivered *before* the energy improvements are complete if the lender denotes that the postponed improvements will be complete within 180 days of the date of the note. Acceptable postponed items are those that do not require an occupancy permit.

The cost of the improvements must not represent more than 10% of the "as completed" appraised value of the property. The Fannie Mae 10% limit does not imply that the appraised value of the energy-efficient improvements cannot exceed 10%. The appraiser must apply the appropriate adjustment based on market support to be in compliance with USPAP. The lending guideline implies that the lender may

---

5. US Department of Veterans Affairs, *Lender's Handbook* (*VA Pamphlet 26-7*). www.benefits. va.gov/warms/pam26_7.asp

not lend more than 10% of the "as completed" appraised value of the property, which becomes an underwriter calculation and not a function of the appraiser.[6]

Market Data Challenges for Energy-Efficient Improvements

As explained previously in this book, most data sources do not provide sufficient data fields to allow appraisers to develop market-extracted adjustments. This problem will be eliminated as more MLS software system vendors incorporate green data fields. The National Association of Realtors requires multiple listing services to adopt the Real Estate Transaction Standard (RETS), which includes green fields. The data will become more consistent as multiple listing services begin to comply with the new standard.

Appraisers do have other methods to support adjustments for energy-efficient building features, as discussed throughout this text. However, most of these tools require data to support each of the steps used in the methods. A good example is support for energy savings on the subject property and comparable sales. Privacy laws and fear of being held liable for energy reporting limit the data available. Even the RESNET National Building Registry of information on rated homes is not available to appraisers, and the data in the registry only began as of July 2012.[7]

Energy audits and energy modeling reports provide anticipated savings that appraisers can use to develop value. It is important that the appraiser receive the entire report and not just a summary. The report provides valuable information on the energy features that can assist in estimating cost and identifying comparable sales characteristics.

The Appraisal Appeal Process

Lenders selling on the secondary market to Fannie Mae and Freddie Mac upload the appraisal report to a Uniform Collateral Data Port (UCDP). The system allows up to three appraisals on the same property. The mortgage file must include the original appraisal and all subsequent appraisals. Supporting documentation for revising the appraisal must be in the mortgage file. Simply put, lenders cannot continue to order appraisals until they receive the value they "need" to make the loan. They must justify ordering a second appraisal.

Lenders are required to provide a copy of the appraisal to the borrower three days prior to the loan closing and any subsequent revisions at closing. Borrowers may waive their right to receive the appraisal within the three-day period. However, even though the borrower receives a copy of the appraisal, that does not make the borrower the appraiser's client.

---

6. *Announcement SEL-2010-15: New Energy Improvement Feature and Other Related Updates* (Washington D.C.: Fannie Mae, December 1, 2010), www.fanniemae.com/content/announcement/sel1015.pdf.

7. Steve Baden (executive director, RESNET), in discussion with the author, September 24, 2013.

Sample Client-Appraiser Relationship

Many appraisers include language like the following in their reports to clarify the client-appraiser relationship:

> The intended user of this appraisal report is the lender/client. No additional intended users are identified by the appraiser. This report contains sufficient information to enable the client to understand the report. Any other party receiving a copy of this report for any reason is not an intended user, nor does it result in an appraiser-client relationship. Use of this report by any other party (or parties) is not intended by the appraiser.

This statement makes it clear that the appraiser's client is the lender. However, this doesn't mean that the borrower cannot question the appraisal. Instead, it simply means that all appraisal-related questions should be presented to the lender, the appraiser's client.

The following language, which originally appeared in the Appraisal Institute seminar *UAD Aftereffects: Efficiency vs. Obligation*, may be provided to a borrower who questions the appraisal:

- All communications from borrowers or third parties must be in writing.
- Disputes must be accompanied by factual information.
- The appraiser will be held harmless by the client for confidentiality issues.
- Unprofessional language or attitudes will not be tolerated.
- Threats or intimidating behavior will be regarded as coercive and referred to the appropriate agencies under AIR.[8]

Appraisal Question or Appeal?

To appeal an appraisal, non-appraisers should keep the following in mind:

- If you have a simple question about clarifying information in the appraisal, put your question in writing and provide it to the lender. The lender should provide the question to the appraiser for a response.

- If an error of fact is found, provide support proving the error and submit it to the lender. The lender should transmit it to the appraiser to make the appropriate changes. Errors that would warrant legitimate questions include the following:
    - Incorrect sales data description
    - Omission of relevant sales (more relevant sales needed)
    - Questionable subject property description
    - Math error
    - Omission of factual information or incorrect information that would materially affect value, such as
        ◦ Solar PV system omitted
        ◦ Incorrect bathroom count

---

8. Dawn Molitor and Richard Heyn, *UAD Aftereffects: Efficiency vs. Obligation* (Chicago: Appraisal Institute, 2012).

- ◦ Incorrect bedroom count
- ◦ Garage omitted
- ◦ Energy efficiency incorrectly rated on high-performance house
- ◦ High-performance features not described or analyzed

It is not appropriate for a borrower, builder, or sales agent to call the appraiser directly about the appraisal report because of the appraiser-client relationship. The lender, rather than the borrower, is the appraiser's client. The lender does not release a copy of the report to the builder or sales agent, and those individuals can only receive a copy if the borrower provides them with one. The builder, borrower, and sales agent should follow the steps above if, upon review of the appraisal, questions occur. However, this does not imply that the appraiser cannot talk with the builder, seller, or sales agent. The appraiser must have communication with these parties to gather pertinent data. Nevertheless, once the appraisal is complete, any follow-up questions should go through the lender.

As an example of a valid reason for an appeal, a homeowner received a copy of an appraisal of a high-performance house with an estimated cost of more than $700,000. The homeowner applied for a mortgage with a large national lender, and the appraisal was completed. The appraisal did not consider the high-performance features. The owner asked the appraiser why he did not use a particular sale in the same neighborhood that was similar in most respects to the property being appraised. The appraiser responded that he had to eliminate that sale because it was the only one in the neighborhood and the bank required three from the same neighborhood. Therefore, he went to a different neighborhood to find three sales.

The homeowner had numerous conversations with the lender after consulting with a local real estate agent. The agent suggested that the homeowner appeal the appraisal with the lender and request a second appraisal from an appraiser with an education in high-performance valuation.

The lender assigned a second appraiser but apparently did not tell this second appraiser that the subject was a high-performance property. When the appraiser called for the appointment and was told that the subject property was high performance, the appraiser gave the agent involved an earful about how green building is political hogwash and that he didn't know what a HERS rating was and didn't care to find out.

The good news in this case is that the appraiser declined the assignment. The bad news is that 30 days later this issue had still not been resolved. It seems that the appraisers in the general area who had taken green valuation courses were not active in this particular market. This scenario also indicates that the lender or AMC did not qualify the appraisers for the assignment.

If lenders and AMCs begin to qualify appraisers based on their education and experience, more appraisers will become qualified. The more that borrowers become aware of their rights in the loan process and insist on a qualified appraiser, the sooner the problem will end. Lenders will get the message that they must qualify appraisers prior to engaging them.

A Reality Check for Builders, Agents, and Homeowners

Why should a high-performance house that does not sell for more than a conventional code-built house be appraised at a higher value than a conventional house? This is a question that many non-appraisers ask.

It is the buyers and sellers in the market, rather than the appraiser, who determine value. The appraiser must develop skills to extract and analyze the data to develop a supported opinion of value. Builders report selling high-performance houses for the same price as code-built houses to avoid holding costs or because they fear the appraised value will not justify the contract price. One builder reported selling a high-performance house for less than the competition in order to gain a market share and higher volume. The builders should not expect higher appraised values than code-built homes if the contract prices do not reflect premiums over the standard code-built house. Through pricing, the high-performance builder may have a shorter marketing period and sell at higher volume, which equates to a lower carrying expense and more profit for the builder.

Builders often ask, "If there are no sales of high-performance houses and my first few houses do not appraise for what I sold them for, what should I do?" The answer is to stay firm with your pricing and prepare the first few buyers to expect that the appraised values may be less than the sale prices for the following reasons:

- High-performance houses are new to the particular market area. Therefore, appraisers do not yet have sales to justify the premium using market data.
- After a few sales of high-performance houses close at these higher prices, data will become available to support higher value conclusions.

Appraisers should also ensure that buyers have a good understanding of the cost-saving benefits of the high-performance features that may not be evident in market data at this point.

The first few purchasers of high-performance houses in a market should have a sufficient down payment so that the sale would not be affected by the appraised value being slightly under the contract price. Ideally, it would be great to have three or four cash sales sold at prices higher than conventional code-built houses to build up the comparable data supporting high-performance prices. Upon the completion of the house and transaction closing, closed sales that meet the definition of *market value* will qualify as comparable sales that will support the higher prices.

Placing a builder sale in the MLS as a bona fide sale when in fact it is a custom high-performance house built on a lot owned by the person having the house built is not an ethical way to build high-performance data in the market. Secondary mortgage market guidelines forbid appraisers from using the combination of a lot value plus the cost to build a house as a comparable sale.[9] This does not meet the definition of market value.

A review of the definition of market value provides further explanation. The following excerpt is from the preprinted statement of assumptions and limiting conditions for the Fannie Mae URAR form that is meant to accompany all appraisal reports made for mortgage lending purposes:

> **Definition of Market Value:** The most probable price which a property should bring in a competitive and open market under all conditions requisite to a fair sale, the buyer and seller, each acting prudently, knowledgeably and assuming the price is not affected by undue stimulus. Implicit in this definition is the consummation of a sale as of a specified date and the passing of title from seller to buyer under conditions whereby: (1) buyer and seller are typically motivated; (2) both parties are well informed or well advised, and each acting in what he or she considers his or her own best interest; (3) a reasonable time is allowed for exposure in the open market; (4) payment is made in terms of cash in U. S. dollars or in terms of financial arrangements comparable thereto; and (5) the price represents the normal consideration for the property sold unaffected by special or creative financing or sales concessions* granted by anyone associated with the sale.
>
> * Adjustments to the comparables must be made for special or creative financing or sales concessions. No adjustments are necessary for those costs which are normally paid by sellers as a result of tradition or law in a market area; these costs are readily identifiable since the seller pays these costs in virtually all sales transactions. Special or creative financing adjustments can be made to the comparable property by comparisons to financing terms offered by a third party institutional lender that is not already involved in the property or transaction. Any adjustment should not be calculated on a mechanical dollar for dollar cost of the financing or concession but the dollar amount of any adjustment should approximate the market's reaction to the financing or concessions based on the appraiser's judgment.[10]

Item 3 from this excerpt indicates that to meet the definitions of *market value* and *arm's-length transaction*, the property must be offered for sale with a reasonable amount of time allowed for exposure in the open market. This would eliminate the combination of the house price with the value of a lot owned or recently purchased by the homeowner.

Item 5 addresses concessions that must be reported and analyzed by the appraiser. If a builder offers a credit card, new car, or free appliances with the purchase of a new home, the appraiser must report these items. (Leased solar PV systems or power purchase agreements that are considered personal property are also concessions.) The appraiser must analyze the sale to determine if these items influ-

---

9. *Selling Guide*, 514.
10. Fannie Mae Form 1004B 6-93, also known as Freddie Mac Form 439 6-93.

enced the sale price. The analysis would be supported by reviewing comparable sales to see if the comparable sales unaffected by these concessions sold for the same price. If they sold for less than a sale with these types of concessions, the data indicates that the buyer paid more for the property because of the concessions. The appraiser must disclose the concessions and make appropriate adjustments or be in violation of the lending guidelines. These types of concessions should be reported in the MLS upon the sale of the property to allow for proper reporting of the items when the sale is used as a comparable in an appraisal report.

If the MLS listings of the high-performance houses are not properly populated, the data may skew the indicated value estimate. The tools from the appraiser's toolbox can provide a reliable value conclusion if accurate and ample data exists and the appraiser has the skills and time to employ them.

Understanding the constraints of the appraisal process will assist real estate professionals in working with appraisers to accomplish credible appraisal results.

ADDITIONAL RESOURCES

Fannie Mae

· See www.efanniemae.com for a complete review of their Appraiser Independence Requirements (AIR). The full AIR document is available at www.fanniemae.com/content/fact_sheet/appraiser-independence-requirements.pdf.

· The most current version of Fannie Mae's single-family *Selling Guide* can be found at www.fanniemae.com/singlefamily/originating-underwriting.

· Appraisers and those who use appraisal services should be familiar with Fannie Mae's document, *Guidance for Lenders and Appraisers*, available online at www.fanniemae.com/content/fact_sheet/appraisal-guidance.pdf. This guide supplements the *Selling Guide* for performing and underwriting property appraisals for Fannie Mae.

Freddie Mac

· The Freddie Mac guidelines for appraisal practices are similar to Fannie Mae's and can be reviewed on the organization's website at www.freddiemac.com.

The Appraisal of an
Energy Star House

The Environmental Protection Agency's Energy Star (ES) program has certified more than 1.4 million homes to date.[1] The Energy Star label is probably the most recognized house label. If you ask buyers or sellers to identify the characteristics of an ES house, they would most likely say it is energy efficient. This is true, and the program has continually increased its energy efficiency requirements as codes have changed. The certification program is currently in its third version, and the organization also offers the Indoor AirPlus program. ES houses that meet the requirements of the Indoor AirPlus program have two of the six elements of green building in place, although this doesn't automatically make the homes green.

Over 20% of the Energy Star-rated homes in the United States are located in Arizona. Well over 6,000 homes are ES certified in Arizona per year. A substantial number of these homes are located in Tucson. Over 50% of all dwellings built in Tucson in 2002 qualified as ES homes.[2]

Some of the characteristics of the different ES guideline versions are provided in Exhibit 8.1, and Exhibit 8.2 shows a timeline of these different versions. The Energy Star website (www.energystar.gov) provides further details on the different versions of the program.

More specifically, Energy Star's Version 3 requirements include the following:

- Energy Star reference design
  A set of core efficiency requirements for the building envelope, HVAC and water heating equipment, lighting, and appliances.

- Variable versus fixed HERS Index score
  Instead of a fixed HERS Index score, a variable HERS Index target score is calculated for each home by applying the efficiency requirements of the Energy Star reference design.

- Size adjustment factor
  Homes larger than the average size for a specified number of bedrooms (known as the "benchmark home size") must apply a size

---

1. Energy Star, www.energystar.gov/homes.
2. Larry Kinney, Howard Geller, and Mark Ruzzin, *Increasing Energy Efficiency in New Buildings in the Southwest: Energy Codes and Best Practices* (Boulder, CO: E-Star Colorado, Colorado Govenor's Office of Energy Management and Conservation, and The Energy Foundation, 2013).

Exhibit 8.1   Energy Star Requirements by Version

Program Version	Date Valid	Requirements
2	Until 1/1/12 for homes that met the requirements before 4/1/11	· Core Version 2 energy-efficiency measures · Thermal bypass checklist
2.5 (transitional)	Until 1/1/12 for homes that met the requirements before 4/1/11	· Core Version 3 energy-efficiency measures · Expanded set of building science checklists— Note that shortcomings in some sections will not prevent homes from qualifying under this transitional specification.
3	Began as of 1/1/12	· Core Version 3 energy-efficiency measures · Expanded set of building science checklists—Note that full compliance is required. · The specific Energy Star prescriptive path used must be identified · The paper trail providing valuation information must be identified

Exhibit 8.2   Timeline of Energy Star Program Versions

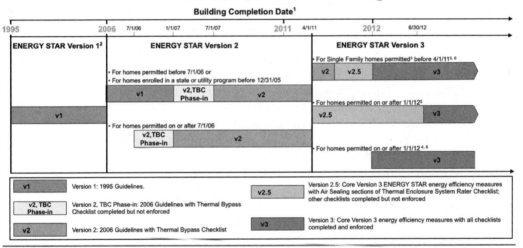

Source: US Environmental Protection Agency, "History of the Energy Star Guidelines for New Homes," www.energystar.gov/index.cfm?c=new_homes.nh_history.

adjustment factor that will reduce the Energy Star HERS Index target and increase the home's energy-efficiency requirements. A house can take credit for renewable energy systems, but only to help larger homes meet the additional efficiency required by the size adjustment factor.

The Energy Star label shown in Exhibit 8.3 should be completed and attached to the inside of the home's electrical panel. This sticker provides good information for appraisers to note in their reports and usually includes a contact name for the rater, who can also provide valuable information to appraisers.

According to the 2010 *Expenditure Consumer Survey* of the Bureau of Labor Statistics, 21% of the amount homeowners spent on their homes annually went to pay utility bills. This represents a significant amount of the overall housing expense. The overall housing expense must consider *all* expenses; this is one of the goals of the SAVE Act, which has been discussed previously in this book. Housing expense includes the following categories:

- Principal
- Interest
- Taxes
- Insurance
- Maintenance, including yard, painting, plumbing, and mechanical repairs
- Utilities, including water, electric, and other energy sources
- Reserves for replacements for major repairs such as roof, HVAC, flooring, and appliances

Exhibit 8.3   Energy Star Label

Many homeowners do not enter into the purchase of a home with a full understanding of the necessary costs for maintaining the home. The SAVE Act is intended to add transparency to this process. When first-time buyers apply for a home loan and know the amount of money they will be expected to pay for their utility bills, they will be more selective in their choice of homes. Data will become more revealing of energy-efficiency premiums as the United States continues to move toward becoming a more energy-independent country.

ENERGY STAR BUILDING SCIENCE CHECKLISTS

Both the Performance and Prescriptive Paths of Version 3 require the completion of four inspection checklists:

- Thermal Enclosure Checklist—must be completed by a home energy rater
- HVAC Quality Installation Checklist—must be completed by a home energy rater
- HVAC Quality Installation Checklist—must be completed by an HVAC contractor
- Water Management Checklist—must be completed by the builder

Currently, a number of builders have been building ES-labeled homes and selling them for the same price as code-built houses. If this pricing path continues, premiums will never be supported by market data. For example, a builder called numerous times to ask me to provide education to appraisers in his area because they were not accounting for additional value for his ES homes. After several conversations in which I explained the steps and costs that would be necessary to offer this type of education, it became clear to the builder that classes were not going to happen at the time. During our last conversation, I learned that the builder sold ES homes and code-built homes in the same subdivision. The next question I asked– "How much more do you sell the ES Homes for compared to the code-built homes?"–ended our series of phone conversations: The builder admitted that the two different types of homes sell for the same amount. He couldn't get an appraiser to appraise the properties for higher values because he wasn't able to market them properly.

Builders develop market comparables that indicate that ES homes sell for the same amount as code-built homes. Until builders are willing to raise prices and find buyers who can invest a large enough down payment so as not to worry about the appraisal amount, ES homes will keep appraising for the same amount as code-built houses. After several ES homes are sold at higher prices, they will begin to appraise for more. As long as the builder doesn't sell ES houses for a premium, they will not appraise at a premium over the code-built house. Keep in mind that appraisers do not add value; instead, they measure value based on market transactions of similar properties.

Excerpts from an Appraisal Report for an Energy Star-Rated Property

The following section presents excerpts from an actual appraisal report and completed Residential Green and Energy Efficient Addendum form that I received from a builder.

The property appraised was proposed construction in South Carolina with a signed contract to build an Energy Star- and EarthCraft-certified house. The builder questioned this appraisal report. He did not see how it reflected the items presented in the addendum. The completed addendum form is shown in Exhibit 8.4 and is followed by extracts from the appraisal report.

Overview of the Appraisal Report

The neighborhood section of this appraisal report does not provide information on energy-efficient or green properties. This would be a good place to begin the green discussion. Providing the reader with information on current market trends sets the foundation for the remainder of the report.

Improvements Section of URAR Form

The completed improvements section of the URAR form from this appraisal report is shown in Exhibit 8.5. The improvements section of the URAR form is a logical place to find a reference to the inclusion of the addendum form and a description of the items found on this form. Based on the completed addendum shown in Exhibit 8.4, it becomes apparent that the only words in Exhibit 8.5 that come near

Exhibit 8.4   Completed Addendum Form

Client File #:		Appraisal File #:	

AI Reports®

Form 820.04*

Residential Green and Energy Efficient Addendum

Client: Confidential

Subject Property: Proposed Construction

City:	State: SC	Zip:

Additional resources to aid in the valuation of green properties and the completion of this form can be found at
http://www.appraisalinstitute.org/education/green_energy_addendum.aspx

The appraiser hereby certifies that the information provided within this addendum:

- has been considered in the appraiser's development of the appraisal of the subject property only for the client and intended user(s) identified in the appraisal report and only for the intended use stated in the report.
- is not provided by the appraiser for any other purpose and should not be relied upon by parties other than those identified by the appraiser as the client or intended user(s) in the report.
- is the result of the appraiser's routine inspection of and inquiries about the subject property's green and energy efficient features. Extraordinary assumption: Data provided herein is assumed to be accurate and if found to be in error could alter the appraiser's opinions or conclusions.
- is not made as a representation or as a warranty as to the efficiency, quality, function, operability, reliability or cost savings of the reported items or of the subject property in general, and this addendum should not be relied upon for such assessments.

Green Building: The practice of creating structures and using processes that are environmentally responsible and resource-efficient throughout a building's lifecycle from siting to design, construction, operation, maintenance, renovation, and deconstruction. This practice expands and complements the classic building design concerns of economy, utility, durability, and comfort.[1] High Performance building and green building are often used interchangeably.

Six Elements of Green Building: A green building has attributes that fall into the six elements of green building known as (1) site, (2) water, (3) energy, (4) materials, (5) indoor air quality, and (6) maintenance and operation. A Green Building will be energy efficient but an energy efficient building is not synonymous with Green Building.

Green Features

The following items are considered within the appraised value of the subject property:

Certification	Year Certified: 2013	Certifying Organization: ☐ Home Innovation Research Labs (ICC-700) ☐ USGBC (LEED) ☒ Other: Southface Earth Craft	☐ Verification Reviewed on site	☒ Certification attached to this report
Rating	Score:285 Gold	☐ LEED Certified: ☐ LEED Silver ☐ LEED Gold ☐ LEED Platinum		
		☐ ICC-700 *National Green Building Standard* Certified: ☐ Bronze ☐ Silver ☐ Gold ☐ Emerald		
		Green Certifying Organization URL (website) www.earthcrafthouse.org		
Additions		Explain any additions or changes made to the structure since it was certified:		
		Do changes require recertification to verify rating is still applicable? ☐ Yes ☐ No		
Comments Attach the rating worksheet that provides the ratings for each element to provide a better understanding of the features. The worksheet will assist in comparing the subject to sales rated by different organizations.		If a property is built green but not formally certified, it still deserves proper description and analysis to value the features. The market analysis is of the structure's physical, economic, and locational attributes and not an analysis of its label alone.		

The objective of this Addendum is to standardize the communication of the high performing features of residential properties. Identifying the features not found on the 1004 form provides a basis for comparable selection and analysis of the features. Builders, contractors, homeowners, and third party verifiers are encouraged to complete this Addendum and present to appraisers, agents, lenders, and homeowners.

---

[1] U.S. Environmental Protection Agency at www.epa.gov/greenbuildings/pubs/about.htm.

*NOTICE: The Appraisal Institute publishes this form for use by appraisers where the appraiser deems use of the form appropriate. Depending on the assignment, the appraiser may need to provide additional data, analysis and work product not called for in this form. The Appraisal Institute plays no role in completing the form and disclaims any responsibility for the data, analysis or any other work product provided by the individual appraiser(s).

AI Reports® AI-820.04 Residential Green and Energy Efficient Addendum   © Appraisal Institute 2013, All Rights Reserved   January 2013

Exhibit 8.4   Completed Addendum Form *(continued)*

Client:		Client File #:	
Subject Property:		Appraisal File #:	

ENERGY EFFICIENT ITEMS

The following items are considered within the appraised value of the subject property:

Insulation	☐ Fiberglass Blown-In ☒ Foam Insulation ☐ Cellulose ☐ Fiberglass Batt Insulation ☐ Other (Describe): ☒ Basement Insulation (Describe): Superior walls with integral foam insulation ☐ HERS Insulation Installed Rating: ☐ 1 ☐ 2 ☐ 3 (See Glossary)	R-Value: ☒ Walls R-20 ☒ Ceiling R-38 ☒ Floor - R-25

Envelope	Envelope Tightness: 1500 Unit: ☐ CFM25 ☒ CFM50 ☐ ACH50 ☐ ACHnatural ☒ Envelope Tightness based on Blower Door Test

Water Efficiency	☐ Reclaimed Water System (Explain): ☐ Greywater reuse system ☐ WaterSense® fixtures	☐ Cistern - Size: Gallons ☐ Rain Barrels Provide Irrigation	Location of cistern:

Windows	☒ ENERGY STAR®	☒ Low E	☐ High Impact	☐ Storm	☒ Double Pane ☐ Triple Pane	☐ Tinted	☐ Solar Shades

Day Lighting	☐ Skylights - #:	☐ Solar Tubes - #:	☐ Other (Explain):				☐ ENERGY STAR Light Fixtures

Appliances	ENERGY STAR® Appliances: ☒ Dishwasher ☒ Refrigerator ☐ Other:	Water Heater: ☐ Solar ☐ Heat Pump ☒ Tankless ☐ Coil Size: Gal.	Appliance Energy Source: ☐ Propane ☒ Electric ☒ Natural Gas ☐ Other (Describe):

HVAC (Describe in Comments Area)	☒ High Efficiency HVAC SEER: 17 Efficiency Rating: % AFUE* % *Annual Fuel-Utilization Efficiency	☒ Heat Pump Efficiency Rating: COP: HSPF: 8.9 SEER: 17 EER:	☒ Thermostat/Controllers Programmable, internet connected	☐ Passive Solar (Defined in Glossary)
	☒ Programmable Thermostat		☐ Radiant Floor Heat	☐ Geothermal

Energy Rating	☒ ENERGY STAR ®Home - Version: 3.0 ☐ Other (Describe): Home Energy Score (HES) (Score range 1-10): ☐ Certification Attached

Indoor Air Quality	☒ Indoor Air PLUS Package	☒ Energy Recovery Ventilator Unit or Whole Building Ventilation System	☒ Non Toxic Pest Control

HERS Information	Rating: 46	Monthly Energy Savings on Rating: $200	Date Rated: 5/16/2013

Utility Costs	Average Annual Utility Cost: $ 170 per month based on: Remrate	# of Occupants: 2

Energy Audit	☐ Infrared Photograph Attached Has an energy audit/rating been performed on the subject property? ☐ Yes ☐ No ☐ Unknown If yes, comment on work completed as result of audit.

Comments (Include source for information provided in this section) Attach documents or reference them in your workfile The energy element is the most measurable element of green or high performance housing.	Information was provided by: Energy Rate

Exhibit 8.4   Completed Addendum Form *(continued)*

Client:		Client File #:	
Subject Property:		Appraisal File #:	

Solar Panels

The following items are considered within the appraised value of the subject property:

Description	Array #1	☐ Leased ☐ Owned	Array #2	☐ Leased ☐ Owned	Description	Solar Thermal Water Heating System
kW (size)					If Active System - type	☐Direct ☐ Indirect
Manufacturer of Panels					If Passive System - type	☐ Integral collector ☐ Thermosyphon
Warranty on Panels					Storage Tank Size	# Gallons:
Age of Panels					Collector Type	☐ Flat-Plat Collector ☐ Integral Collector ☐ Evacuated-Tube Solar
Energy Production kWh per Array						
Source for Energy Production Estimate					Back-Up System	☐ Conventional Water Htr ☐ Tankless On Demand ☐ Tankless Heat Pump
Location (Roof, Ground, Etc.)					Age of System	
Tilt/Slope for Array					Warranty Term	
Azimuth per Array					Manufacturer	
Age of Inverter(s)					Solar Energy Factor (SEF) (Rating range 1 to 11 - higher number is more efficient)	
Manufacturer						
Warranty Term						

Name of Utility Company:		Cost per kWh charged by Company: $ /kWh

Comments (Discuss incentives available for new panels, condition of current panels, and any maintenance issues. If leased, provide the lease terms.) A free online tool and manual for valuing the energy production of the Solar PV System is available at www.pvvalue.com Download the PV Value™ Manual for explanation of the solar terms on this form and inputs used in the PV Value Tool.	Discuss source of information and define other renewable energy sources, such as wind, hydropower, biomass power, etc. No solar

Exhibit 8.5   Completed Improvements Section of URAR Form

General Description	Foundation	Exterior Description	materials/condition	Interior	materials/condition
Units ☒ One ☐ One with Accessory Unit	☐ Concrete Slab ☐ Crawl Space	Foundation Walls	Block/Brick/New	Floors	Cpt/Hdw/Ti/New
# of Stories	☒ Full Basement ☐ Partial Basement	Exterior Walls	Brick Veneer/New	Walls	Drywall/New
Type ☒ Det. ☐ Att. ☐ S-Det/End Unit	Basement Area 2,633 sq. ft.	Roof Surface	Arch Shingle/New	Trim/Finish	Wood-Pntd/New
☐ Existing ☒ Proposed ☐ Under Const.	Basement Finish 73 %	Gutters & Downspouts	Aluminum/New	Bath Floor	Tile/New
Design (Style) Traditional	☐ Outside Entry/Exit ☐ Sump Pump	Window Type	Vinyl SH/New	Bath Wainscot	Tub Surround/New
Year Built 2013	Evidence of ☐ Infestation	Storm Sash/Insulated	Insulated/New	Car Storage ☐ None	
Effective Age (Yrs) 0	☐ Dampness ☐ Settlement	Screens	Combo/New	☒ Driveway # of Cars 2	
Attic ☐ None	Heating ☒ FWA ☐ HWBB ☐ Radiant	Amenities	☐ Woodstove(s) #	Driveway Surface Concrete/New	
☒ Drop Stair ☐ Stairs	☐ Other Fuel Gas	☒ Fireplace(s) # 1 ☐ Fence None		☒ Garage # of Cars 3	
☐ Floor ☐ Scuttle	Cooling ☒ Central Air Conditioning	☒ Patio/Deck Both ☒ Porch Front		☐ Carport # of Cars 0	
☐ Finished ☐ Heated	☐ Individual ☐ Other	☐ Pool None ☐ Other None		☒ Att. ☐ Det. ☐ Built-in	

Appliances ☐Refrigerator ☒Range/Oven ☒Dishwasher ☒Disposal ☒Microwave ☐Washer/Dryer ☐Other (describe)

Finished area **above** grade contains: 7 Rooms   2 Bedrooms   2.0 Bath(s)   2,774 Square Feet of Gross Living Area Above Grade

Additional features (special energy efficient items, etc.)

   Open Front Porch, Uncovered Concrete Patio, Uncovered Wood Deck, Energy Efficient, etc. ◄━━━━━━━━

Describe the condition of the property (including needed repairs, deterioration, renovations, remodeling, etc.).

   C1; No upgrades in the prior 15 years. The subject is a proposed construction single family home. The plans and specifications supplied by the client were reviewed for this appraisal assignment. The subject suffers no functional or external obsolescence. Appraisal report is subject to completion per plans and specifications on the basis of a hypothetical condiiton that the improvements have been completed.

Are there any physical deficiencies or adverse conditions that affect the livability, soundness, or structural integrity of the property? ☐ Yes ☒ No If Yes, describe

   Physical deterioration is limited to normal wear and tear. The appraiser does not perform the same level of inspection as a professional home inspector. No physical deficiencies or adverse conditions were found during the normal appraisal inspection of the subject property.

Does the property generally conform to the neighborhood (functional utility, style, condition, use, construction, etc.)? ☒ Yes ☐ No If No, describe

   The subject generally conforms to the neighborhood in functional utility, style, use and construction. No functional or external obsolescence was nothed during the inspection of the subject property.

addressing anything on the addendum are the words *energy efficient*, which are indicated by the arrow.

Sales Comparison Approach Section of URAR Form

The completed sales comparison approach section of the URAR form from the appraisal report is shown in Exhibit 8.6. Here, the same two words–*energy efficient*–are used to describe the subject property and all the comparable sales. In the *Other* line item, *None* is reported for the subject and the sales. Six comparable sales were used, but only three representative sales are provided on this part of the form. Comparable Sale 2 is six years old, and Comparable Sale 3 is eight years old. Comparable Sales 4, 5, and 6 are 9-, 10 , and 12-year-old structures. No additional comments are made on the form to provide an understanding of the energy-efficient items in any of the six sales used. Building codes and HERS Index ratings have changed dramatically in the past 6 to 12 years. Are these older homes equal in energy efficiency to the subject property, which has a HERS Index rating of 46 as well as an EarthCraft rating? Because the subject property is proposed construction, the ratings are preliminary and subject to a final confirmation upon completion. These ratings are not mentioned in the appraisal report.

The comments in the sales comparison approach section of the URAR form provide the sales search parameters as follows:

> The initial comparable sale search focused on sales, listings, and pending sales with transaction dates within the past three months, located within 2+/-miles of the subject, of similar GLA, site size, age, and design.

Exhibit 8.6 Completed Sales Comparison Approach Section of URAR Form

FEATURE	SUBJECT	COMPARABLE SALE # 1		COMPARABLE SALE # 2		COMPARABLE SALE # 3	
Functional Utility	Acceptable	Acceptable		Acceptable		Acceptable	
Heating/Cooling	FWA C/Air	FWA C/Air		FWA C/Air		FWA C/Air	
Energy Efficient Items	Energy Efficient	Energy Efficient		Energy Efficient		Energy Efficient	
Garage/Carport	3 Car Garage	2 Car Garage	3,500	2 Car Garage	3,500	2 Car Garage	
Porch/Patio/Deck	OFP, Deck, Patio	OFP, Deck, Patio		OFP, Deck, Patio	1,000	OFP, OBP	
Fireplace(s), etc.	1 F/P	1 F/P		2 F/P	-1,250	2 F/P	0
Fence, Storage	None	None		None		Fence	-1,250
Other	None	None		None		None	-1,100

> The initial search resulted in seven sold properties and 15 active listings. The search parameters were then expanded to transaction dates over three months but less than six months in sale date using the same physical characteristics.

Did the search criteria indicate energy-efficient and green-rated homes as a feature? Based on the description above, it is unlikely. Notice that up to this point the report has not mentioned the EarthCraft certification or the addendum form that was completed by the builder.

Cost Approach Section

In the appraisal report, the cost approach section does not include charges or physical, functional, or external loss. The sources for the cost data used are Marshall & Swift/Boeckh, builders, and appraisals. The comments in the URAR form do not address energy-efficient or green features. The reported value by this approach is 20% higher than the value by the sales comparison approach without a comment on the higher value indication.

Final Value Conclusion

The appraised value in the report is based on the cost and sales comparison approaches. The two approaches indicate two different values with a 20% spread. This spread in indications is wider than what is typically seen. The Appraisal Institute textbook *Appraising Residential Properties* provides the following advice on this type of variance:

> Each valuation approach serves as a check on the other approaches used. *A wide variation among the value estimates derived often suggests that one approach is not as applicable as the others or that valuation procedures have not been properly applied* [emphasis added]. Unrealistic conclusions must be closely scrutinized. Once the appraiser is satisfied that the general range of value indications is justified, each indication is weighted according to its appropriateness and reliability. Finally, the appraiser selects a single value opinion or a range of value opinions based on the market data and on informed judgment.[3]

Conclusion of the Lender-Underwriter

The appraisal report passed through the review process of the lender. The borrower received a copy of the appraisal report and passed it on to the builder, who was shocked at its shortcomings.

3. *Appraising Residential Properties*, 4th ed. (Chicago: Appraisal Institute, 2007), 85.

How Should the Report Have Been Documented?

An appraisal report should tell one story throughout the entire report. The following sections of the URAR form are areas where high-performance features should be addressed for a well-documented, consistent report.

Neighborhood Section

The neighborhood section of the appraisal report is where the story begins. In this section, market trends for properties like the subject should be discussed. In this case, a discussion of the number of high-performance or green-rated houses built in this market area and neighborhood sets the stage for the sales comparison approach. If this is the first green-rated house in the market area or neighborhood, it alerts the underwriter that sales of other high-performance homes will not be available.

Site Section

The site section should refer the reader to the Residential Green and Energy Efficient Addendum. The addendum completed by the builder includes details about the property's orientation, landscaping, and Walk Score. For some high-performance properties, special irrigation or site features may require additional comment.

Improvements Section

The improvements section of the report should refer the reader to the special energy-efficient section of the addendum. The addendum includes discussions of numerous energy-efficient items that are important to understanding the overall energy efficiency of the structure. Fannie Mae requires that energy-efficient items be described.

Sales Comparison Approach Section

The sales search criteria should include a search for sales of properties with similar high-performance features. If sales of homes with similar features are not available, an explanation is expected. For instance, if the neighborhood section indicates that the number of high-performance houses is increasing in the neighborhood but no high-performance sales are used, this does not necessarily mean that there is an inconsistency. The high-performance homes may be custom-built and would not meet the definition of market value because they were not exposed to the market and were built based on a contract between the landowners and the builders. However, if this is the case, explanation should be provided to avoid the appearance of inconsistency.

Using an older comparable sale of a high-performance home as the fourth, fifth, or sixth comparable sale would be desirable. This would provide an indication of the market's acceptance of the high-performance property. It would also show the diligence exercised by the appraiser to use similar sales.

The sales grid on the URAR form offers three blank lines where appraisers can describe additional property features that should be analyzed. This would be the perfect place to describe the HERS Index rating, Energy Star and other green certifications, and other special features.

The summary of the sales comparison approach section of the URAR form should discuss the analysis of the high-performance features. Support should be provided for the adjustments. If no adjustment is made for these features, the appraiser is indicating that he or she decided (based on prior analysis) to make an adjustment of zero. Zero is still a number and requires just as much analysis and support as any other adjustment.

Cost Approach Section

The cost approach should be consistent with the sales comparison approach. An appraisal of a high-performance house should use appropriate cost figures from the green section of the current Marshall & Swift/Boeckh *Residential Cost Handbook.* If a local builder's cost is used, the report should indicate whether or not that builder is constructing high-performance houses. If the neighborhood section of the report indicates that the subject property is the first one built in this market area, how could other local builders provide "comparable cost data"? The discussion of the cost approach should indicate that the energy-efficient features have been included in the cost features. In new construction, the cost approach is relevant because buyers are comparing costs as well as existing housing prices. Cost is market related. However, it cannot be given the sole weight in the appraisal report for a secondary mortgage market transaction.

How This Story Ended

The lender, builder, and original appraiser continued a dialogue for several weeks about this appraisal. The builder was diligent in researching the market to verify the sales used by the appraiser and putting his concerns in writing. The loan officer was under the impression that a new appraisal could not be ordered and told the builder that once an appraisal is completed it stays with the property forever. This was a misconception on the loan officer's part. The builder searched the secondary mortgage market guidelines to prove that the loan officer's statement was incorrect.

The lender assumed that the original appraiser was competent in handling this assignment. However, the lender did not question the appraiser's experience or education prior to assigning the appraisal. In this case, the ordering department told the appraiser to make adjustments for energy efficiency if other sales of energy-efficient homes could not be found. The lender was not able to reconcile the original appraisal and ordered a second appraisal from a different appraiser who admitted a lack of competency but willing to research the facts to arrive at a supported value. The second appraisal resulted in a value estimate that was closer to the contract price but failed to meet the secondary mortgage market guidelines for a number of reasons, which may have included a lack of similar sales, distant sales, or excessive adjustments. A lender who does not sell mortgages on the secondary mortgage market would have more readily accepted this loan.

These types of deals are difficult for all parties involved, and they usually result in the deal falling through when borrowers are not aware of their rights in the process. This particular builder did his homework on the appeal process. However, if the lender had been qualified prior to making the application, the ending to this story might have been different. Much of the problem was due to a lack of knowledge of the process from beginning to end. As the industry moves forward with high-performance house transactions, this problem should gradually diminish. However, it takes time and diligence to work through the bumps in the road.

CALL TO ACTION

Write the appraisal report considering the knowledge of the intended user. The typical client in the market has limited (if any) knowledge of high-performance buildings, and the appraiser is responsible for writing reports to the typical client's level of understanding. Describe the basics of high-performance features and their benefits. Provide resources within the report that the client can easily research to gain a better understanding of the property type and special problems the property may present in the marketplace. As high-performance properties become more prevalent in the market, clients will become more knowledgeable about this property type. This will make appraisers' jobs easier.

The Appraisal of a Passive
Solar House

A passive solar home collects heat as the sun shines through its south-facing windows and retains it in materials that store heat, which are known as *thermal mass* materials. These materials may include concrete, brick, stone, or tile. They absorb heat from sunlight during the heating season (hot weather) as well as heat from warm air in the house during the cooling season (cold weather).

The windows or other devices that collect solar energy should face within 30 degrees of true south and should not be shaded during the heating season by other buildings or trees between 9 a.m. and 3 p.m. each day. Exhibit 9.1 illustrates the concept of thermal mass during the heating season.

The solar heat must be collected and stored in different areas, using conduction, convection, and radiation. Fans and blowers help distribute heat. Conduction occurs when heat moves between two objects that are in direct contact with each other, such as when a sun-heated floor warms your bare feet. Convection occurs when heat is transferred through a substance, such as air or water. Passive solar homes often use convection to move air from warmer areas—a sunspace, for example—to the rest of the house. Radiation is what you feel when you stand next to a wood stove or a sunny window and feel its warmth on your skin.

Some strategies for heat control in a passive solar house include

- Properly sized roof overhangs that provide shade to vertical south-facing windows during the summer months
- Electronic sensing devices, such as a differential thermostat that signals a fan to turn on operable vents and dampers that allow or restrict air flow, low-emissivity blinds, operable insulating shutters, and awnings.[1]

The following five elements constitute a complete passive solar building design:

- Aperture (collector)
  The aperture is made up of large glass areas where sunlight can enter the building. Typically, apertures should face within 30 degrees

---

1. US Department of Energy, http://energy.gov/energysaver/articles/passive-solar-home-design.

Exhibit 9.1   Thermal Mass in the Heating Season

THERMAL MASS IN THE HEATING SEASON

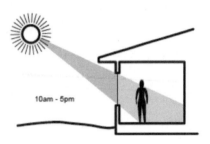

10:00 am to 5:00 pm

Sunlight enters south-facing windows and strikes the thermal mass inside the home. The sunlight is converted to heat energy, which heats both the air and thermal mass materials. On most sunny days, solar heat maintains comfort during the mid-morning to late afternoon periods.

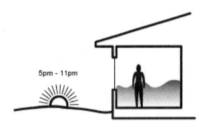

5:00 pm to 11:00 pm

As the sun sets, it stops supplying heat to the home. However, a substantial amount of heat has been stored in the thermal mass. These materials release the heat slowly into the passive solar rooms, keeping them comfortable on most winter evenings. If temperatures fall below the comfort level, supplemental heat is needed.

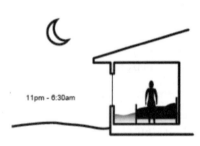

11:00 pm to 6:30 am

The home owner sets the thermostat back at night, so only minimal back-up heating is needed. Energy-efficient features in the home minimize heat losses to the outside.

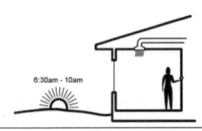

6:30 am to 10:00 am

The cool early morning hours are the toughest for passive solar heating systems to provide comfort. The thermal mass has usually given up most of its heat, and the sun has not risen enough to begin heating the home. During this period, the home owner may have to rely on supplemental heat. Energy-efficient features in the home minimize the need for supplemental heating.

Source: "Passive Solar Design: Increase Energy Efficiency and Comfort in Homes by Incorporating Passive Solar Design Features (Technology Fact Sheet)" (Washington, D.C.: US Dept. of Energy, Office of Building Technology, State and Community Programs, Energy Efficiency and Renewable Energy, 2000), http://apps1.eere.energy.gov/buildings/publications/pdfs/building_america/29236.pdf.

of true south and should not be shaded by other buildings or objects between 9 a.m. and 3 p.m. each day during the heating season.

- Absorber
Absorption is usually accomplished using masonry walls, floors, or water containers that sit in the direct sunlight.

- Thermal mass
A thermal mass is needed to absorb, store, and distribute heat.

- Distribution
Distribution is a method of circulating solar heat from the collection and storage points to the different areas of the building

- Control
During the summer months, the aperture area requires control or shading to eliminate the heat. This can be accomplished with roof overhangs, solar shades, or awnings.

Each element performs a separate function, but all five elements must work together in order for the passive solar design to be successful.

Passive solar buildings have some similarities to net-zero energy and high-performance buildings. The envelope is tightly sealed and well insulated in all of these types of buildings. However, a home with a passive solar design is heated by passive solar gain and internal gains from people and electrical equipment. Auxiliary heat sources are often achieved through small sources, such as wood pellet stoves, ductless heat pumps, and baseboard electric heat.

A passive solar structure avoids heat gain via shading and window orientation that limits any cooling load. The term *orientation* refers to the direction that a building faces. However, special views are gained through proper placement of doors and windows. Building a passive solar house on a site with a special view that would command a premium requires a special design to avoid losing this amenity.

To improve the indoor air quality in a tightly sealed building, an energy recovery ventilator provides a constant, balanced fresh air supply. The type of ventilator system used in a particular building is based on climate.

Some types of passive solar systems that use the sun's heat without interference and that provide heat collection, storage, and distribution within the same space are called *direct gain systems*. A direct gain system includes south-facing windows and a large mass placed within the space to receive the most direct sunlight in cold weather and the least direct sunlight in hot weather. In this type of system, sunlight passes through the windows and its heat is trapped by the thermal mass in the room. In cool weather, the mass absorbs solar heat during its exposure to direct sunlight and radiates that heat back into the space, most notably at night.

According to Sustainable Sources' Passive Solar Design website (http://passivesolar.sustainablesources.com), the cost of a house with passive solar elements is similar to that of conventional building

This photo shows an exterior view of a passive solar house.

Photo appears compliments of Stitt Energy Systems, Inc.

This photo provides an interior view of the passive solar house shown above.

Photo appears compliments of Stitt Energy Systems, Inc.

designs. Costs of some internal thermal mass materials, such as stone and brick, add to the total cost but add aesthetic enhancements. Sustainable Sources' Passive Solar Design website also has a wealth of other information on passive solar structures.

The popular perception of passive solar structures is often inaccurate. Passive solar design does not require an unusual or unique style. The accompanying photographs show good examples of passive solar structures that do not differ in style from other houses in a typical residential neighborhood.

Supporting Documents for Passive Solar Houses

Most new passive solar houses have a HERS Index score that provides the energy-efficiency rating of the house compared to the local code. The HERS report provides an estimate of the annual utility costs.

Some passive solar houses may have earned a certification from an organization such as PHIUS, or Passive House Institute US (www.passivehouse.us). To earn the PHIUS Plus Certification, a house must meet a thorough passive house design verification protocol and pass an on-site quality assurance and control test given by a PHIUS rater. The quality assurance and control test includes a blower door test, a ventilation balancing and commissioning test, and verification of the HERS Index score. Certification documents can provide valuable information on construction and energy modeling.

Handling Difficulties in the Valuation of Passive Solar Houses

Passive solar houses have been built in this country for many years, and more will be built as energy efficiency becomes more of a political and cultural focus. However, these properties present complex appraisal problems because there are usually few comparable sales within the same market area, resulting in few (if any) sales for comparison. These homes may also include features such as wind, geothermal, or solar heating and energy generation systems that are difficult to quantify with sales data but that add significant costs to the project. Appraisers should be able to explain the passive solar design in terms that are meaningful and at a level the client can understand. This lays the groundwork for the analysis and level of difficulty of the appraisal problem. Most intended users in the lending world have limited knowledge of passive house design, making the appraiser responsible for articulating features and special benefits in detail.

An exterior view of another passive solar house is shown in this photograph.

Photo appears compliments of Stitt Energy Systems, Inc.

In addition, appraisers should define the appraisal problem in a manner that emphasizes the existence of passive solar design in the market area. A review of building permits or a call to the local homebuilders association might be helpful in estimating the number of homes in the area. Discussing the number of homes built and the number of resales in the appraisal report provides a basis for the explanation of the difficulties encountered during the sales comparison approach.

When receiving an order for an appraisal of a passive solar house from a lender, appraisers should alert the lender that this sort of property appraisal may not meet secondary mortgage market guidelines. For example, the sales comparison approach may be less than reliable, and the cost approach may be more credible. (Keep in mind that secondary mortgage market guidelines do not allow appraisers to rely solely on the cost approach.) In a case like this, sales of net-zero energy or net-zero electric homes, Energy Star homes, green-certified houses, or houses with low HERS Index ratings would be acceptable comparables. If direct market evidence with paired data analysis is not available to support an adjustment for the differences between the different types of structures, consider developing an estimate of the cost difference between the structures. Support the higher cost of building passive solar over code-built structures with an income capitalization technique of energy savings differences. Verify the energy costs on all comparable properties and use that as a basis for an

This photo shows an interior view of a different passive solar house.

Photo appears compliments of Stitt Energy Systems, Inc.

income capitalization calculation of the present value of the energy saved over a projected period of time. This may be the typical occupancy period or life of the loan, the useful life of the energy features, or some other logical time period that can be explained. Be sure to explain and support the discount rate. A discount rate for a residential property might be similar to that of an alternative investment or the 30-year fixed Fannie Mae mortgage rate, or it might reflect the responses from a survey indicating the return buyers might expect on an investment. Show the math used in the DCF analysis and compare the results from those derived from different methods, reconciling to a supported opinion of value. Using more than one method to support an energy adjustment provides a test of reasonableness that should always be included in the analysis.

Analysis or consideration of studies published in other areas of the country that provide general percentage premiums over code-built houses provide acceptable tests of reasonableness but should not be used as the sole support for an adjustment. Most studies are based on statistical techniques that the appraiser may not understand or feel comfortable in explaining. If the appraiser has not researched the basis of the study or the author's credibility and does not understand the methodology used, the study should not be relied on for developing adjustments.

Use the Residential Green and Energy Efficient Addendum to guide your site visit and gather pertinent description details. If the house uses solar photovoltaic energy, the addendum will provide the solar inputs needed to use the PV Value software (www.pvvalue.com) discussed in detail in Chapter 6 of this book.

Tools to use for defending adjustments or the lack of adjustments for energy or other differences were also discussed earlier in this text. The typical underwriter will want appraisers to use another "comparable" sale of a passive solar structure. In most markets, there will be limited sales data to accommodate this request. However, using a dated sale or active listing may provide a solution. Using two or more methods to estimate the value of the property will be necessary to prove adjustments for the energy efficiency of the house.

The passive solar house presents appraisers with a complex appraisal problem in most market areas because of the limited number of comparable sales. Passive solar design is not a new product in the market, but homes with passive solar designs still make up a small percentage of the overall housing stock. Appraisal assignments involving passive solar houses require an appraiser with specialized expertise, a client who is willing to pay a commensurate appraisal fee, and possibly a lender who is willing to keep the loan in house. The following real-life case study involves a passive solar house that was under contract but for which no willing appraiser could be found to take on the assignment. This case study illustrates the need for appraisers with skills in these complex areas.

Case Study

A two-story passive solar house (shown in the accompanying photograph) with 3,400 square feet of living area went under contract in the fall of 2013. The house was 15 years old at the time and is located three miles from a small town with a population of 1,777. The house has an interior rock wall that functions as thermal mass material for the sun that enters through large, south-facing windows. The house has two wood pellet stoves with thermostat controls as a back-up heating source. In 15 years, the interior temperature during the day had never dropped below 50 degrees Fahrenheit. The house is located in Wyoming, where temperatures often drop below zero. The wood pellets used for heating the house and 1,000-sq.-ft. garage area cost *$200 per year*. The typical house of this size in this market experiences heating costs of *$400 per month*.

This photograph shows the passive solar house described in the case study.

Photograph appears compliments of Melanie B. Fullman.

The house is connected to the electric grid. Due to high winds in this area, electrical blackouts are common. However, this house continues to have heat from the solar design and wood pellet backup system during these electrical blackouts.

The contract price exceeded $400,000, and the loan amount was $250,000. The borrower was required to obtain an appraisal, and the lender planned to keep the loan in house. It did not need to meet secondary mortgage market guidelines. Over a four-month period, numerous calls were made to appraisers who practiced within a few hundred miles of the house. No appraiser was willing to accept this assignment. The buyers offered to provide the design plans and a thorough thermal evaluation of the structure from a licensed engineer and to pay any additional fees necessary to complete the appraisal report. The engineer told the buyers that given the property's geographic location (latitude, elevation) and design (passive solar, first floor positioned three-quarters of the way into the ground, etc.), there was no way the temperature inside the house would ever fall below 50 degrees Fahrenheit. The engineer offered to provide a report with calculable proof of the home's solar integrity. Still, the lender was not willing to accept the engineer's statements, and no appraiser would accept the assignment.

What Reasons Did the Appraisers Give for Not Accepting This Assignment?

Most appraisers cited a lack of comparable properties when declining this assignment. One appraiser cited that he did not want to accept the assignment because he would be held liable if the house froze and the water pipes broke.

What Are Some Other Reasons That Might Have Discouraged Appraisers from Accepting This Assignment?

The appraisers in this case may have been concerned that the appraisal fee could not possibly compensate for the amount of time needed to complete the assignment. They may have also been concerned about their lack of knowledge of passive solar design or lack of the necessary competency to meet USPAP standards. Finally, these appraisers may have simply thought that this assignment was too difficult to tackle.

How Would an Appraiser Begin to Estimate a Fee for This Type of Complex Problem?

It would be logical for the appraiser to consider the amount of time needed to inspect the property, research the market, and write the report. The appraiser could estimate how many typical appraisal assignments could be done in that same amount of time and total the fees for that number of assignments as a starting point for estimating the fee for this special type of assignment.

The buyer of this property eventually found a lender who would portfolio the loan (keeping it in house) and not sell it on the secondary mortgage market. The buyers decided to purchase large electric wall heating units (for $3,000) so that they could move beyond the appraisal and complete the loan. After these heating units (which were not actually needed) were installed, an appraiser was willing to appraise the house. The loan process took eight months because of these difficulties. Since the new owners have occupied the house they have spent a total of $100 on wood pellets for the three wood stoves in the winter of 2013-2014. The outdoor temperature on a cold day in February 2014 was -20 degrees Fahrenheit in the morning and -4 degrees in the afternoon, and the interior of the house as of 5:30 p.m. on that day was 71 degrees.

This case study clearly indicates that there is demand for skilled appraisers who are willing to tackle tough assignments. Skilled appraisers should expect fees that are commensurate with the complexity of the appraisal problem, the amount of time involved in the assignment, and the professional liability that comes with the assignment. In this particular case, the buyers were willing to pay for professional service and time was not an issue, considering it took a total of eight months to close the loan and cost the buyers an additional $3,000 for unnecessary heating units.

Valuation Issues in the Appraisal of Homes with Solar Photovoltaic Systems

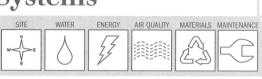

10

SITE   WATER   ENERGY   AIR QUALITY   MATERIALS   MAINTENANCE

Valuing houses with solar photovoltaic (PV) systems presents complex appraisal problems. Solar PV systems vary widely, and appraisers are required to have knowledge of energy production capabilities and installation requirements in order to arrive at credible value conclusions.

Solar PV systems have been installed on residential properties since as early as the 1970s. However, technology has changed dramatically and installation prices have decreased significantly since then. Incentives are available to offset the initial system costs, which has encouraged installations of PV systems across the country. States with high energy costs or enticing incentives have seen the most growth in this area.

In some cases, solar PV systems are leased, which can create additional valuation challenges as discussed later in this chapter. In these cases, the *lessor* is the party that owns the solar PV system, the *lessee* is the property owner that leases a solar PV system from a third party or solar company, and the *host* is the property owner that has title to the property and leases space (rooftop or other) to a solar company. Exhibit 10.1 lists some commonly used acronyms for various solar PV-related terms.

Property Assessed Clean Energy (PACE) financing is available in some states to allow homeowners to borrower money to buy and install equipment that makes homes more energy efficient. Repayment of the loan is facilitated through special assessments on property taxes. Some PACE financing programs become senior liens on the properties. As a result, the senior lien would be paid prior to the mortgage if a default or foreclosure occurred. This has caused secondary mortgage market problems with refinancing homes with PACE liens that would have a senior lien position. It also presents problems in the case of the sale or transfer of a property to a buyer assuming the PACE loan who needs a mortgage but cannot obtain the mortgage if the PACE loan trumps the mortgage. In many cases, the seller is required to pay off the PACE loan prior to selling the property to a borrower who needs a mortgage. The alternative for a seller

Exhibit 10.1   Solar PV Acronyms

Acronym	Full Term	Explanation
REC	renewable energy credit	RECs are attributed to renewable energy sources. One REC is given for every 1,000 kilowatt-hours of electricity placed on the grid.
SREC	solar renewable energy credit	SRECs are attributed to solar energy produced based on 1 SREC for every 1,000 kilowatt-hours of electricity placed on the grid.
PBI	performance-based incentive (or production-based incentive)	PBIs are cash payments for the number of kilowatt-hours generated by a renewable energy system, such as wind or solar.
FMV	fair market value	FMV represents a transaction between the third party (solar company) and the homeowner regarding the solar PV system (not the property it is attached to).
PPA (or SPPA)	power purchase agreement (or solar power purchase agreement)	In a PPA, a homeowner purchases the energy produced by a solar PV system that is owned by a solar company and placed on the homeowner's roof. PPAs allow property owners to purchase solar power from a third party (solar PV company) for a specified period and at a given price per kilowatt-hour.
TPO	third party-owned	In a TPO system, a solar PV company owns the system and rents the rooftop for a specified period of time. The property owner may or may not be purchasing the energy produced by the system.
TOU	time of use	Rates for electricity change according to the TOU in order to reduce the use of expensive peaker power plants, which are designed for periods when demand is highest.

with a PACE loan that trumps the mortgage who needs the buyer to assume the loan is to seek a cash buyer. However, a cash buyer may not be available in some markets and price ranges. The Center for Sustainable Energy California has good information about the PACE program and the difficulties it has encountered, including California's challenges to the Federal Housing Finance Administration (FHFA) ruling in 2012 that prohibited Fannie Mae and Freddie Mac from purchasing any mortgages with PACE liens.[1] Not all PACE loans are set up in this manner, requiring the real estate professionals involved in PACE loan transactions to know the details of PACE in their areas.

An appraiser must review transactions involving PACE loans carefully on the appraisal property and the comparable sales used. If the buyer assumes the PACE loan, the property price may be less than the sales in which the seller paid off the PACE loan. Adjustments may be necessary, depending on what the market data supports. Multiple listing services do not usually report these details, requiring appraisers to research the public records and/or contact the listing or sales agent to understand how the PACE loan was handled in the sale contract.

California, Arizona, New Jersey, Colorado, and Pennsylvania are the states that have the most solar PV system installations. However, the number of installations is increasing in Oregon, Connecticut, Hawaii, and other states that offer incentives or PACE programs or that have high electrical costs. Solar leasing is becoming popular in some

---

1.   Center for Sustainable Energy California, http://energycenter.org/policy/property-assessed-clean-energy-pace.

states and has been driving the market for residential installations. The growing number of PV system installations and the multiple ownership and financing options that are currently available create new challenges for residential appraisers.

When a property feature is new to the market, it is only logical that sales data on this feature would not be readily available. In the case of solar PV systems, appraiser competency is not usually attained quickly in local markets. The perfect valuation storm is created out of the combination of the previously mentioned difficulties associated with this new feature, limited data, differences in leased versus owned systems, and the limited number of loans made in the past on properties with solar PV systems. Lenders, AMCs, and underwriters are not familiar with these features or the nuisances that are involved. This places more responsibility on the appraiser to write the report to the level of knowledge of the intended user.

One appraiser I spoke with had the following to say about appraisals involving solar PV systems:

> The biggest and most popular fad in green housing right now is solar PV systems. Due to the lack of data, it is next to impossible to value PV systems by paired data. As an alternative, I've been using the Sandia National Laboratories' discounted cash flow PV Value software (www.pvvalue.com), which results in complaints from the borrower that the PV system is valued too low and complaints from the lender that it's valued too high. I'm dealing with this issue right now. I valued a PV solar system via Sandia, and the lender says I need to "take out" the PV solar value because I have no paired data. The borrower (an attorney), on the other hand, threatened to sue me because the PV solar value wasn't high enough. He doesn't know that the lender has asked that the PV value be removed, and I can't tell him because of confidentiality protocols.

If the appraiser in this case follows the underwriter's request to remove the value of the solar PV system, the appraisal is being made subject to a hypothetical condition, which is defined in the 2014-2015 edition of USPAP as

> A condition, directly related to a specific assignment, which is contrary to what is known by the appraiser to exist on the effective date of the assignment results, but is used for the purpose of analysis.
>
> Comment: Hypothetical conditions are contrary to known facts about physical, legal, or economic characteristics of the subject property; or about conditions external to the property, such as market condition or trends; or about the integrity of data used in an analysis.[2]

Appropriate wording for the appraiser to use in the report for this assignment would be something like the following:

> The appraised value is subject to a hypothetical condition that the solar PV system does not exist when in fact it does.

If an appraiser follows the underwriter's request as well as USPAP guidelines, the lender will most likely reject the loan because

---

2. *Uniform Standards of Professional Appraisal Practice*, 2014-2015 ed. (Washington, D.C.: The Appraisal Foundation, 2014), U-3.

the report is then based on a hypothetical condition and not an as is value required by the Interagency Appraisal and Evaluation Guidelines for regulated lending purposes. The appraiser cannot "win" on this deal, and neither can the borrower.

Appraisers must be willing to educate clients who request this type of action. Appraisers should assume that the lender/client (intended user) has limited knowledge of properties with green features. Therefore, appraisers should write more detailed reports to explain the features that make the property different and how the features do or do not benefit the user. Because it is your appraiser's license that is in jeopardy, it is important to understand the guidelines in order to assist the client in understanding your limitations. Simply referencing the USPAP requirement that addresses this situation may help the client agree with your position and arrive at an appropriate decision.

Some appraisers report that clients have asked them to

- Remove energy-efficient adjustments because the underwriters do not allow them
- Appraise the house as though it were code built and ignore the green features
- Remove the value of the solar PV system because there are no comparable sales with these systems
- Remove the Residential Green and Energy Efficient Addendum from the report

All of these requests would result in a hypothetical condition *if* the appraiser had support for the items noted. The underwriter has flexibility in the assignment and can adjust the value outside the report without making demands on the appraiser that would lead to a report that is not in compliance with USPAP. Although the Appraisal Institute's Residential Green and Energy Efficient Addendum is not a secondary mortgage market form, it is not forbidden by the secondary market. It is the appraiser's responsibility to include the necessary documents and forms to produce a credible appraisal report.

Solar Photovoltaic Valuation Tools

A number of methods for supporting adjustments have been used by appraisers for more than 50 years. However, in many cases loan underwriting practices have removed all but one method from the process. Paired data analysis is the only method that many underwriters accept for valuing solar PV systems. The same is true of other energy-efficient or green features.

PV Value software (previously discussed in Chapter 6 of this book) was developed by Sandia National Laboratories and Energy Sense Finance as a tool for developing the DCF of the solar PV energy produced by a system to arrive at a market value range. This tool was originally an Excel-based spreadsheet and modeled similarly to the discounted cash flow used on commercial properties for income streams. The results are inserted into the appraisal report along with support of the data inputs and should be supported by a secondary method as a test of reasonableness. Ideally, this secondary method would be paired data analysis. However, the cost approach or results from national studies are often quoted in the absence of paired sales. The income capitalization approach would not be questioned for commercial properties, but it may become a major lender underwriting issue for residential properties. As discussed earlier in this text, Fannie Mae and Freddie Mac previously published forms using the income capitalization approach to develop the present value of energy savings for residential properties. The income capitalization approach was further validated in the study *The Impact of Photovoltaic Systems on Market Value and Marketability*.[3] This study used PV value software on 30 case studies and found that it yielded results within reason of paired sales analysis.

If the appraiser is required to remove the solar PV value, the report is then based on a hypothetical condition and is not an "as is" value required by the Interagency Appraisal and Evaluation Guidelines for regulated lending purposes. Simply stated, the secondary market would not accept an appraisal based on a hypothetical condition such as this. If the appraiser does not appropriately label it as such, the appraiser might not be in compliance with USPAP.

Unfortunately, many of the most qualified residential appraisers have left the mortgage lending market because of these issues. Competent appraisers can find work outside of the mortgage market, where they don't have to face the same pressures, lower fees, and unreasonable requests that do not fall within USPAP or the 2010 Dodd-Frank Wall Street Reform and Consumer Protection Act. They can instead find valuation or consulting clients in the areas of litigation, estate planning, taxation matters, or other real estate-related services.

Threats to remove appraisers from the "approved" list for not complying with an underwriter's or client's request to remove value that has been supported are not acceptable under the Dodd-Frank Bill. However, fighting the system can be costly, resulting in many experienced professional appraisers seeking clients outside the lending field. What is an appraiser to do? One solution is to choose your clients carefully, Appraisers should be sure that their findings have been documented to result in credible reports and stay current on educational opportunities to enhance analytical skills.

Networking with other professionals is a great way to brainstorm valuation issues and learn about what your peers would do in applicable situations. This valuation issue will get better as sales begin to occur to validate alternative methods.

---

3.   Lisa K. Desmarais, *The Impact of Photovoltaic Systems on Market Value and Marketability* (Colorado Energy Office, 2013), www. colorado.gov.

The Sales-Pitch Formula Used for Selling Solar PV Systems

The following formula is often presented to homeowners in the solar PV system sales pitch. An example is provided using figures appropriate for the Las Vegas area. Appraisers should consider the rationale that buyers and sellers use in making their purchase decisions. However, if the rationale is flawed or only represents a minority of buyers' decisions, it should not be considered during the appraisal process.

Step 1   Obtain electric costs.

Example: $0.12 per kilowatt (Las Vegas area)

Step 2   Estimate the number of annual peak sun hours in the region.

Example: 2,500 peak sun hours in the Las Vegas region

Step 3   Determine the size of the array.

Example: 5 kilowatt (kW) array

2,500 hours × each 1 kW array = 2,500 kilowatt hours

2,500 kWh × $0.12 kWh costs = $300

Step 4   Keeping in mind that the average-sized residential PV system is 5 kW, determine the energy produced and the monetary value of that energy. Then determine the monetary value of the energy produced over the estimated life of the system and the monetary value of the system. Finally, keeping in mind that electricity costs will increase and the estimated life will decrease as the system ages, determine the value of the system as it ages by reducing the estimated life and valuing the aged system.

Example: Energy produced:

5 kW × $300 per kW = $1,500 worth of electricity

$1,500 × 25 years (estimated life) = $37,500 value of energy produced and value of the system

(25 years new − current age of system) × increased electric rate to value aged system

---

What is missing from the above formula? To put it another way, would you pay $150,000 today for a $100,000 house that may be worth an estimated $150,000 in 25 years? The answer is obviously no. This is what the formula suggests by indicating that the value of the solar PV system today is the lump sum of the estimated energy produced over a 25-year period. A prudent homeowner would not pay in one lump sum for the next 25 years of energy use today without expecting a discount.

Another flaw in this formula is that it appears that the energy production may be based on the energy production on the first day or first year using the highest potential amount of sun hours for a given day. It is not realistic to assume that the solar PV system will produce at the same rate every day or that the number of sun hours will be the same every day. These types of observations can quickly assist the client in understanding the results of the "sales-pitch formula" versus the results of a DCF model.

Comparing the Sales-Pitch Formula with DCF Analysis

What is wrong with the sales-pitch formula? The following are some concerns that appraisers and their clients should have about this formula.

- It doesn't consider the time value of money. If you borrowed money, you would have to pay interest, which suggests that money has value over time.

- It doesn't consider a risk or inflation factor. Most lenders have risk factored into their rates. There is no guarantee that the PV system will produce the exact amount shown; it could turn out to be more or less.

- It doesn't consider the type of panel used. Monocrystalline silicon panels have the highest efficiency rate. Polycrystalline panels are less efficient than monocrystalline silicon panels but also less costly than monocrystalline silicon panels. Thin film panels are less efficient than monocrystalline or polycrystalline panels.

- It doesn't indicate whether the mount is fixed or rotating.

- It doesn't provide the azimuth angle (i.e., the angle between due south and the direction the collector faces) or tilt (i.e., the angle that the collector surface makes with the horizontal plane. (Both are expressed in degrees.)

- It doesn't consider the replacement of an inverter or maintenance costs.

- It doesn't consider a degradation rate or derate factor. The *degradation rate* is the loss in energy as the panel ages. The *derate factor* is the loss of electricity throughout the system attributed to the panels, inverter, and cables that each have their own inefficiencies. It is true that improvements have been made in the manufacturing process over the years. However, recent research by the National Renewable Energy Laboratory demonstrates that the energy output of higher-quality crystalline silicon modules degrades at an annual average rate of 0.8% and a median rate of 0.5%, based on a study of 2,000 degradation rates. The majority of systems–78% of all data used in the study–reported a degradation rate of less than 1% annually. The rate of yearly degradation is closer to 1% for some thin film modules.[4] While this doesn't make much of a difference in production for the first few years of the system's life, it can make a significant difference in the value indication after more than 25 years.

- It doesn't consider whether there is shading on part of the PV panels.

Considering these factors sets the stage for developing a present worth formula or DCF analysis of the energy produced, making up for the weaknesses of the sales-pitch formula.

---

4.   D.C. Jordan and S.R. Kurtz, *Photovoltaic Degradation Rates–An Analytical Review* (National Renewable Energy Laboratory, 2011), http://onlinelibrary.wiley.com.

First, consider which discount rate is appropriate. How would a residential user consider the time value of money? An informal survey of appraisers and homeowners indicated that the discount interest rate should be similar to the 15- or 30-year mortgage rate (3.38% to 4.48%), an equity loan (6.16%), and an alternative investment (such as a fairly safe fund at 5%). The interest rates were obtained from local lending and investment sources. These answers all suggest a rather close range of rates. In this case, 4.5% will be used. Appraisers should continually survey their local market to understand the homeowner's thoughts on the discount rate or time value of money. The basis for the discount rate should be explained in the appraisal report.

The degradation rate is an estimate based on the manufacturer's estimates found in the owner's paperwork. The derate factor is already considered in the energy production estimate. The DCF uses a 25-year period that is based on the warranty of the PV system. The projected inflation rate is based on the 25-year escalation rate of retail rates. The loss factor considers a reserve to replace the inverter in Year 15, the cost of monitoring, and minimal repairs. The rates should also be explained in the appraisal report.

The following two DCF models (Exhibits 10.2 and 10.3) both support values for this 5 kW solar photovoltaic system near $20,000.

Reconciliation of Microsoft Excel DCF and PV Value Software

Comparing the two DCF models to the sales-pitch formula clearly shows the error in the sales-pitch methodology.

Tool	Value Indication
Microsoft Excel DCF	$20,000
PV Value software	$19,100 to $22,460
Sales-pitch	$37,000

The gross cost for the 5 kW system in 2011 was $5.50 per watt or $27,500 (5 kW × 1,000 watts per kW × $5.50 per watt = $27,500). The difference between the value indication of the DCF model and the cost can be attributed to superadequacy or functional obsolescence, a category of depreciation. Without incentives to offset the gross cost, the PV system costs more than its contributory value (i.e., the change in the value of a property as a whole, whether positive or negative, resulting from the addition or deletion of a property component) of around $20,000. The present value (worth) of energy production or paired sales, if available, should be compared to the cost of the solar PV system ($27,500 cost less $20,000 contributory value based on the DCF results in a $7,500 difference or category of depreciation on Day 1). This example indicates that a superadequacy or incurable functional obsolescence exists because the system is new and would not have physical depreciation from age. This may change as the market acceptance of solar PV systems increase and the cost of solar PV systems continues to decrease. The price of solar has already decreased to less than $4.00 per watt as of January 2014.

Exhibit 10.2   Valuing a Solar PV System Using Discounted Cash Flow Analysis

Assumptions

System rated capacity	5 kW DC
System age	0 months
Warranty	25 years
Historical production	– kWh since inception
Average monthly production	789 kWh per mo.
Degradation (est.)	0.5% per year
Average electricity cost	$0.120 per kWh
Projected inflation (electricity)	3.5% per year
Loss factor*	5.0% per year

Analysis Year	Annual Electric Output (kWh)	Average Electricity Cost ($/kWh)	Avoided Electricity Cost per Yr.	Loss (1) Factor 5.0%	Net Benefit
1	9,468	$0.120	$1,136	($57)	$1,079
2	9,421	$0.124	$1,169	($58)	$1,111
3	9,374	$0.128	$1,204	($60)	$1,144
4	9,327	$0.133	$1,239	($62)	$1,177
5	9,280	$0.137	$1,275	($64)	$1,212
6	9,234	$0.142	$1,313	($66)	$1,247
7	9,187	$0.147	$1,351	($68)	$1,284
8	9,142	$0.152	$1,391	($70)	$1,321
9	9,096	$0.157	$1,432	($72)	$1,360
10	9,050	$0.163	$1,474	($74)	$1,400
11	9,005	$0.168	$1,517	($76)	$1,441
12	8,960	$0.174	$1,561	($78)	$1,483
13	8,915	$0.180	$1,607	($80)	$1,527
14	8,871	$0.186	$1,654	($83)	$1,572
15	8,826	$0.193	$1,703	($85)	$1,618
16	8,782	$0.200	$1,753	($88)	$1,665
17	8,738	$0.206	$1,804	($90)	$1,714
18	8,695	$0.214	$1,857	($93)	$1,764
19	8,651	$0.221	$1,912	($96)	$1,816
20	8,608	$0.229	$1,968	($98)	$1,869
21	8,565	$0.236	$2,025	($101)	$1,924
22	8,522	$0.245	$2,085	($104)	$1,981
23	8,479	$0.253	$2,146	($107)	$2,039
24	8,437	$0.262	$2,209	($110)	$2,098
25	8,395	$0.271	$2,274	($114)	$2,160

Present value at	4.50%	Annual discount rate	$20,219
Rounded:			**$20,000**
GBA (sq. ft.)			1,800
Contributory value per sq. ft.			$11.23
Implied capitalization rate (Year 1 income / PV)			5.62%

* Loss factor considers costs of monitoring, replacement of PV inverters, etc.

Exhibit 10.3   PV Value Software Solution

| Energy Sense Finance | Sandia National Laboratories | PV Value® | Photovoltaic Energy Valuation Model v. 1.1 |

Choose Property Type   ● Resider Townhouse   [Single-family / Duplex/Villa / Condo]   ○ Commercial

Solar Resource Calculation		Discount Rate Calculation	
Zip Code	89106	Basis Points (low)	50
System Size in Watts	5,000	Basis Points (high)	200
Derate Factor	0.850	Basis Points (average)	125
Commissioning report # is required to override default derate factor		Choose Net Yield Rate	
Commissioning Report #		[FNM 30-Year Fixed 60-day / FNM 15-Year Fixed 60-day / Custom]	8/9/2013
Module Degradation Rate	0.5		
Array Type	Fixed		3.96
Array Tilt (unchecked = latitude)	0.0		
Array Azimuth (default = South)	180	Discount Rate (low)	4.46
kWh Produced/Year		Discount Rate (average)	5.21
9,469		Discount Rate (high)	5.96

Appraisal Range of Value Estimate		
Low	$	19,058.17
Average	$	20,659.31
High	$	22,461.19

Incentives assist in offsetting the obsolescence that would otherwise be seen in the value indication of the application of the cost approach. The value indication from the sales comparison approach would already have factored in the obsolescence. The contributory value in the cost approach and adjustments in the sales comparison approach should be similar.

Appraisers may use the net cost of the solar PV system in the cost approach (gross cost less incentives available as of the effective date of the appraisal equals net cost). However, the appraiser should explain that the cost is net and report the type and amount of incentives. Market value should not consider tax credits that are available to the property owner because they are based on the homeowner's personal property tax position and not the real estate. It is important to explain that personal tax credits were available and are a factor in the homeowner's decision-making process in purchasing a system. The incentives available as of the date of the appraisal can be found on the Database of State Incentives for Renewables and Efficiency (DSIRE) website, www.dsireusa. org. If net cost is used, obsolescence should not be charged to it unless the market indicates that the obsolescence or market penalty is higher than the incentives. (The market penalty is the difference between the gross costs and contributory value extracted from the market on a new system.) If gross cost is used, obsolescence may be required if the price of solar is more than the market is willing to pay based on sales data.

Appraising a property for insurance replacement cost would require the gross cost to be used because there is no guarantee that the incentives will still be available in the future. As the cost declines, the incentives will also decline. According to the DSIRE, the 30% federal income tax credit is scheduled to cease as of December 31, 2016, unless Congress decides to renew. IRS Form 5695 should be used for residential energy credits. Ideally, the DCF analysis should be compared to direct market data, such as paired data analysis. The appraiser is required to support the inputs used in the DCF to add credibility. The gross rent multiplier is usually not a useful tool for the value of solar PV systems. However, it should be tested in your market for validity.

Solar PV Leases

Leased solar PV systems present an additional appraisal dilemma. A number of residential solar PV leases reviewed in 2013 indicate in their lease agreements that the systems arc considered personal property. The contracts reviewed were for 20-year terms, and the solar company rather than the homeowners retains title to the systems. In these cases, the homeowner agrees to pay the annual personal property tax and all other required taxes on the system and maintain an Internet connection to allow the solar company to monitor the system's production. The homeowner also agrees not to mortgage, pledge, lien, or do anything to encumber the security interest of the solar leasing company. The homeowner agrees to allow the solar leasing company to borrow money on the system, transfer title to another, and enter the property to maintain the system as needed. The lease amounts depend on the size of the system, the geographical location, and various terms in the lease.

The residential appraiser must document these lease details as well as the characteristics of the solar PV system and any effect it might have on the market value of the appraised property. It should not be included in the real estate value if it is declared personal property and not in the same ownership as the property. Current secondary mortgage market guidelines do not specifically address solar PV systems, but they do address personal property.

According to Fannie Mae's *Selling Guide Updates and Additional Guidance on Appraisal-Related Policies*, "Lenders are reminded that personal property, including (but not limited to) furniture, vehicles, boats, floating boat docks, and art work, may not be included as additional security for any mortgage on a one-unit property unless otherwise specified by Fannie Mae."[5]

Fannie Mae will be issuing an update to their *Selling Guide*, but it may not address solar PV leasing yet. The secondary mortgage mar-

---

5. *Announcement SEL-2010-09: Selling Guide Updates and Additional Guidance on Appraisal-Related Policies* (Washington, D.C.: Fannie Mae, June 30, 2010), www.fanniemae.com/content/announcement/sel1009.pdf.

ket, FHA, and VA are still researching their positions on solar leases, including power purchase agreements (PPAs).

Personal property is permitted as part of the security for a loan on a two- to four-unit property to the extent that it is pledged by Fannie Mae's 1-4 Family Rider, Form 3170. Whether an item is real or personal property is generally determined by the law of the jurisdiction in the area where the property is located. A professional appraiser who has the knowledge, experience, and geographical competence to complete an appraisal assignment must also possess the expertise to identify personal property items in the appraisal.

It is my opinion that Fannie Mae's guide for one- to four-family properties implies that personal property that is part of the security for the loan can be pledged, but it does require a special rider. It is also important to refer to the lease agreement that often forbids property owners from encumbering the solar PV system with a mortgage or additional lien. Keep in mind that this guide also requires competency before accepting the assignment.

According to the US Department of Housing and Urban Development's *Valuation Protocol* guide, "If the sale involved personal property (such as an above ground pool, lawn mower, furniture, etc.) it should be identified and excluded from the valuation."[6] This guide does not name solar PV systems specifically, but it implies that a leased solar PV system would be included in the personal property category based on the personal property language in contracts and agreements of leased systems or PPAs and the fact that the solar system is not in the homeowner's name.

A PPA is entered into when the homeowner purchases the power (per kWh generated) produced from the PV system for a specified period with renewal options. The term of the agreements reviewed varies between 10 and 20 years. A solar PV company agrees to rent the rooftop of a residential home at $1 or some nominal amount per year. In turn, the solar company agrees to maintain the system, monitor the production, and guarantee the amount of production each year. The homeowner agrees to pay all documented taxes, fees, or charges assessed or charged to the solar company by any governmental authority and pay all taxes owed resulting from the rebates the solar company received for the installation or energy produced. Some PPAs give the solar PV company rights to the renewable energy credits. The language in these leases is not standard, requiring the homeowner and real estate professionals involved to review it carefully.

The appraisal assignment is complicated for the appraiser when a solar PV system is leased or a PPA is involved. Much of the problem is due to a lack of disclosure on the part of the solar industry. The lease or PPA may not be recorded, and there is currently no central database for identifying leased systems or PPAs. Appraisers or real

---

6.   *Appendix D: Valuation Protocol* (4150.2) (Washington, D.C.: US Department of Housing and Urban Development, January 2006), www.hud.gov/offices/adm/hudclips/handbooks/hsgh/4150.2/41502appdHSGH.pdf.

estate agents may incorrectly assume that a system is owned when it is merely leased or a PPA is in place. Multiple listing services should have a searchable field for these leased systems and PPAs. The leased systems and PPAs should be clearly identified in the sales contracts, and whether the buyer assumed the lease agreement or the seller or buyer purchased the system included in the sales contract price should be indicated. These details could affect the value conclusions presented by the data when analyzed by the appraiser.

The solar PV property presents many new scenarios that many appraisers, lenders, and sales agents have not encountered. This new feature is growing rapidly in many markets and requires all of the parties involved in the real estate industry to communicate on the issues discussed in this chapter. Some standardization is needed in the solar industry to solve many of the problems discussed.

ADDITIONAL RESOURCES

Solar Energy Terms

The US Department of Energy's Solar Energy Glossary contains definitions for technical terms related to solar power and PV technologies. The glossary can be found at www1.eere.energy.gov/solar/sunshot/glossary.html.

Renewable Energy Credits

The National Renewable Energy Laboratory's website, www.nrel.gov, provides information on renewable energy credits.

Performance-Based Incentives

The Database of State Incentives for Renewables and Efficiency website, www.dsireusa.org, contains many examples of available performance- or production-based incentives.

PACE Financing

More information about PACE program financing is available on the US Department of Energy's Database of State Incentives for Renewables and Efficiency website at www.dsireusa.org/solar and the Center for Sustainable Energy California's website at http://energycenter.org/policy/property-assessed-clean-energy-pace.

PV Value Software

More information on PV Value software, which is discussed throughout this book, as well as a free download of the software itself can be found at www.pvvalue.com

The Appraisal of a Net-Zero Energy or Net-Zero Electric House

11

A net-zero energy building produces as much energy as it uses and has a HERS Index rating of zero. This is accomplished through the use of some or all of the following features:

- A tightly sealed, well-insulated envelope
- Alternative energy sources such as solar, geothermal, and wind power
- High-efficiency mechanicals
- Passive heating and cooling design elements (such as passive solar, day-lighting, and natural ventilation) that reduce the energy load

Exhibit 11.1   A Net-Zero Energy House

Typically, newly built net-zero energy buildings such as the house shown in Exhibit 11.1 are designed to use 50% less energy than a code-built home. Homes that are renovated or retrofitted for net-zero energy typically aim for a 30% reduction of energy use from the code requirements.[1] The energy remainder is made up by on-site generation from renewable sources such as solar PV systems.

Net-zero electric houses should not be confused with net-zero energy houses. A net-zero electric building produces as much electricity as it uses. However, the building's heating source may not be electric. The owner may have gas, oil, or another type of heating source. However, few net-zero electric houses exist and present the same valuation problems as net-zero energy buildings, although their popularity may increase with time.

Exhibit 11.2   A Net-Zero Electric House

1.   Zero Energy Design, P.C., www.zeroenergy.com/zehland.html.

A net-zero electric house is pictured in Exhibit 11.2. From a street view, the house has appeal similar to a conventional-built home.

Difficulties in the Valuation of Net-Zero Energy and Net-Zero Electric Houses

Net-zero energy and net-zero electric homes are popping up in many areas of the country. These properties present complex appraisal problems because there are often few comparable sales within the same market area. These homes also have features such as wind, geothermal, or solar power and heat-generating systems that can be difficult to quantify with sales data but that add significant costs to the project.

Appraisers should define the appraisal problem with an emphasis on the existence of net-zero energy or net-zero electric buildings in the market area. A review of building permits or a call to the local homebuilders association might be helpful in estimating the number of homes in the area. Discussing the number of homes built and the number of resales in the appraisal report provides a basis for explaining the difficulties found in the application of the sales comparison approach. Keep in mind that net-zero energy or net-zero electric buildings also incorporate passive design features such as daylighting, passive solar systems, and natural ventilation. These features may not be readily apparent to the appraiser, particularly those unfamiliar with sustainable design.

At the time of accepting the assignment, the appraiser should alert the lender that the appraisal may not meet secondary mortgage market guidelines. The appraiser should explain that although the secondary mortgage market does not allow appraisers to rely solely on the cost approach, this approach may be more credible if the sales comparison approach is less than reliable. The comparable sales used may not be net-zero energy or electric homes, and direct market support for adjustments through paired sales analysis may not be possible. This may result in the need to use an alternative, but proven, appraisal method to develop an adjustment for energy savings. An early discussion with the lender's underwriter may save the appraiser from making time-consuming revisions later. The appraiser should only accept the assignment if he or she has competency in this property type, as required by the secondary mortgage market and the Federal Housing Administration. For more information, appraisers are encouraged to reference the US Department of Energy's brochure titled *DOE Challenge Home & The Appraisal Process: Be Your Own Advocate.*[2] More articles and brochures are being published by various parties to alert the market of their right to a competent appraiser.

---

2. Sam Rashkin, *DOE Challenge Home & The Appraisal Process: Be Your Own Advocate* (Washington, D.C.: US Department of Energy, Energy Efficiency & Renewable Energy), http://www1.eere.energy.gov/buildings/residential/pdfs/ch_appraisal_process.pdf. Sam Rashkin is the Chief Architect of the US Department of Energy's Building Technologies Program. The brochure is not dated but it appears to have been developed in 2013 because it references the most recent version of the Appraisal Institute's Residential Green and Energy Efficient Addendum.

The analysis or consideration of studies published in other areas of the country that provide general percentage premiums for net-zero energy or net-zero electric homes over code-built homes are acceptable tests of reasonableness but should not be the sole support for an adjustment.

Using the Residential Green and Energy Efficient Addendum to guide the site visit and gather pertinent description details is invaluable in the appraisal of net-zero energy or electric homes. If the house uses solar PV energy, the addendum will provide the solar inputs needed to use the PV Value tool discussed earlier in this text (and available at www.pvvalue.com).

Tools to defend adjustments or a lack of adjustments for energy efficiency or other differences have been discussed throughout this text. The typical underwriter will want the appraiser to use another "comparable" sale of a net-zero energy or net-zero electric property. In most markets, there will be limited sales data to accommodate this request. Using two or more methods to estimate the value of this type of property is necessary to prove adjustments for the energy efficiency of the house.

The following documents can be used as support for energy savings estimates:

- HERS Index rating (or full HERS report for new construction)
- Completed Residential Green and Energy Efficient Addendum with the structure's energy features adequately documented
- Utility bills and occupant interviews (to illustrate that the bills are representative of typical users) for existing homes
- Discussion and documentation of energy production for homes that use alternative energy sources (The Residential Green and Energy Efficient Addendum may be used for solar PV systems.)
- Occupant interviews in which occupants discuss their knowledge of other net-zero energy or net-zero electric houses in the area

Appraisers should seek comparable sales of high-performance houses in the absence of net-zero energy or net-zero electric property sales. Houses with low HERS Index ratings should be used and the energy use of the comparable properties compared to the net-zero property should be thoroughly analyzed. Be careful not to "double-count" when adjusting for energy efficiency and solar PV production. The solar PV or alternative energy source may be what brought the house from a low HERS Index rating to zero. Therefore, you may consider the alternative energy source in the adjustment for energy efficiency. Underwriters do not have preferences as to which line in the sales comparison approach is used to apply the adjustment so long as it is explained and supported.

Exhibits 11.3, 11.4, and 11.5 show completed portions of the Residential Green and Energy Efficient Addendum and the URAR form (Fannie Mae Form 1004) that support the adjustments made in the ap-

General Description		Foundation		Exterior Description	materials/condition	Interior	materials/condition
Units [X] One ☐ One with Accessory Unit		☐ Concrete Slab ☐ Crawl Space		Foundation Walls	Concr Block/Good	Floors	Hdwd/Cpt/good
# of Stories		[X] Full Basement ☐ Partial Basement		Exterior Walls	Fr/Hardboard/good	Walls	Drywall/good
Type [X] Det. ☐ Att. ☐ S-Det/End Unit		Basement Area	1,200 sq. ft.	Roof Surface	Metal/good	Trim/Finish	Wood Cove/good
[X] Existing ☐ Proposed ☐ Under Const.		Basement Finish	90 %	Gutters & Downspouts	Aluminum/good	Bath Floor	Tile/good
Design (Style)	Salt Box	☐ Outside Entry/Exit [X] Sump Pump		Window Type	Low-E/good	Bath Wainscot	Tile/good
Year Built	2010	Evidence of ☐ Infestation		Storm Sash/Insulated	Low-E/good	Car Storage	☐ None
Effective Age (Yrs)	3	☐ Dampness ☐ Settlement		Screens	Aluminum/good	[X] Driveway # of Cars 2	
Attic	☐ None	Heating [X] FWA ☐ HWBB ☐ Radiant		Amenities	☐ Woodstove(s) #	Driveway Surface	
[X] Drop Stair	☐ Stairs	☐ Other	Fuel Electric	[X] Fireplace(s) # 1	☐ Fence	[X] Garage # of Cars 2	
☐ Floor	☐ Scuttle	Cooling [X] Central Air Conditioning		☐ Patio/Deck	☐ Porch	☐ Carport # of Cars	
☐ Finished	☐ Heated	☐ Individual	☐ Other	☐ Pool	☐ Other	[X] Att. ☐ Det. ☐ Built-in	

Appliances [D]Refrigerator [X]Range/Oven [X]Dishwasher [X]Disposal [X]Microwave [D]Washer/Dryer ☐Other (describe)

Finished area **above** grade contains: 8 Rooms   4 Bedrooms   3 Bath(s)   2,400 Square Feet of Gross Living Area Above Grade

Additional features (special energy efficient items, etc.)   See attached AI Residential Green and Energy Efficient Addendum for energy efficient details

Describe the condition of the property (including needed repairs, deterioration, renovations, remodeling, etc.).   The property is in good repair with no items of deferred
    maintenance visible.

Are there any physical deficiencies or adverse conditions that affect the livability, soundness, or structural integrity of the property? ☐ Yes [X] No If Yes, describe

Does the property generally conform to the neighborhood (functional utility, style, condition, use, construction, etc.)? [X] Yes ☐ No If No, describe The structure is a
    net-zero energy house meaning it produces as much energy as it uses. It is connected to the public utility company and has a 5 kW solar photovotaic system that provides
    electricity throughout the house. This is the first net-zero energy house in this neighborhood and it will have lower maintenance costs than other houses because of the
    energy efficient features shouwn on the attached Addendum

plication of the sales comparison approach for a hypothetical net-zero energy home.

The comparable sales search in this case included the defined neighborhood and entire market area for sales of properties with similar energy-efficient characteristics. The search perimeters included the requirements that the sales be from the last year and of 1- or 1.5-story houses that were built within the last five years with between 2,100 and 2,600 square feet of living area. The three sales in Exhibit 11.5 are the most recent sales of homes that had energy-efficient attributes, although they are not net-zero energy houses like the subject property. The market has been stable over the past 12 months, so no adjustment for market conditions is required.

A half-bath adjustment is developed at $2,000, based on the depreciated cost and a paired data analysis. The gross living area adjustment is based on a paired data analysis of properties of similar age in the same neighborhood. The data does not support an adjustment for minor differences in houses between one and five years old. The minor differences in the base size and finish did not affect sale prices, so no adjustment is applied for basement differences.

Comparable Sale 1 is built to a similar energy rating as the subject property but does not have solar PV panels. The only adjustments necessary to this sale are those for square footage, energy efficiency (i.e., solar PV production), and the lack of a half-bath.

ENERGY EFFICIENT ITEMS

The following items are considered within the appraised value of the subject property:

Insulation	☐ Fiberglass Blown-In ☒ Foam Insulation ☐ Cellulose ☐ Fiberglass Batt Insulation ☐ Other (Describe): ☒ Basement Insulation (Describe): Icynene spray ☒ HERS Insulation Installed Rating: ☒ 1 ☐ 2 ☐ 3 (See Glossary)	R-Value: ☒ Walls 22 ☒ Ceiling 41 ☐ Floor

Envelope	Envelope Tightness: Unit: ☐ CFM25 ☐ CFM50 ☒ ACH50 ☐ ACHnatural ☒ Envelope Tightness based on Blower Door Test

Water Efficiency	☐ Reclaimed Water System (Explain): ☐ Greywater reuse system ☐ WaterSense® fixtures	☐ Cistern - Size: Gallons ☐ Rain Barrels Provide Irrigation	Location of cistern:

Windows	☐ ENERGY STAR®	☒ Low E	☐ High Impact	☐ Storm	☐ Double Pane ☐ Triple Pane	☐ Tinted	☐ Solar Shades

Day Lighting	☐ Skylights - #:	☐ Solar Tubes - #:	☐ Other (Explain):	☒ ENERGY STAR Light Fixtures

Appliances	ENERGY STAR® Appliances: ☒ Dishwasher ☒ Refrigerator ☐ Other:	Water Heater: ☒ Solar ☐ Heat Pump ☐ Tankless ☐ Coil Size: Gal.	Appliance Energy Source: ☐ Propane ☐ Electric ☐ Natural Gas ☐ Other (Describe):

HVAC (Describe in Comments Area)	☒ High Efficiency HVAC SEER: 19 Efficiency Rating: 98 % AFUE* % *Annual Fuel-Utilization Efficiency	☐ Heat Pump Efficiency Rating: COP: HSPF: SEER: EER:	☒ Thermostat/Controllers	☐ Passive Solar (Defined in Glossary)
	☐ Programmable Thermostat		☐ Radiant Floor Heat	☐ Geothermal

Energy Rating	☐ ENERGY STAR®Home - Version: ☐ Other (Describe): Home Energy Score (HES) (Score range 1-10): ☐ Certification Attached

Indoor Air Quality	☐ Indoor Air PLUS Package	☒ Energy Recovery Ventilator Unit or Whole Building Ventilation System	☐ Non Toxic Pest Control

HERS Information	Rating: 0	Monthly Energy Savings on Rating: $	Date Rated:

Utility Costs	Average Annual Utility Cost: $ 0 per month based on:	# of Occupants:

Energy Audit	☐ Infrared Photograph Attached Has an energy audit/rating been performed on the subject property? ☐ Yes ☒ No ☐ Unknown If yes, comment on work completed as result of audit.

Comments (Include source for information provided in this section) Attach documents or reference them in your workfile The energy element is the most measurable element of green or high performance housing.	Information was provided by: Owner provided copies of the actual utility bills before and after installing the solar PV system. Those bills are in the appraiser's workfile. The structure was built in 2010 with a low HERS Index rating of 56. After installing the solar PV system three months ago, a rater performed another HERS test to verify that the house had a HERS Index of 0. A copy of the most recent HERS Index report is attached to this report. The envelope tightness rating is 3 ACH50. This envelope (walls, floors, roof, doors, and windows) rating is tighter than the standard code-built home requirement of 7 ACH50, based on the 2009 IECC and adopted locally. Because of the tightness of the envelope, the house has an energy recovery ventilation system to control air movement as needed.

Solar Panels

The following items are considered within the appraised value of the subject property:

Description	Array #1	☐ Leased ☒ Owned	Array #2	☐ Leased ☐ Owned	Description	Solar Thermal Water Heating System
kW (size)	5 kW				If Active System - type	☐ Direct ☐ Indirect
Manufacturer of Panels	Mage Solar (Dublin, GA)				If Passive System - type	☐ Integral collector ☐ Thermosyphon
Warranty on Panels	20 Years				Storage Tank Size	# Gallons:
Age of Panels	2013—new				Collector Type	☐ Flat-Plat Collector ☐ Integral Collector ☐ Evacuated-Tube Solar
Energy Production kWh per Array	7,702 kWh					
Source for Energy Production Estimate	PV Value estimate				Back-Up System	☐ Conventional Water Htr ☐ Tankless On Demand ☐ Tankless Heat Pump
Location (Roof, Ground, Etc.)	Roof				Age of System	
Tilt/Slope for Array	unknown				Warranty Term	
Azimuth per Array	180				Manufacturer	
Age of Inverter(s)	3 noths old				Solar Energy Factor (SEF) (Rating range 1 to 11 - higher number is more efficient)	
Manufacturer	Fronius USA					
Warranty Term	10 years					

Name of Utility Company: XYZ Utility Co.	Cost per kWh charged by Company: $0.1185/kWh

Comments (Discuss incentives available for new panels, condition of current panels, and any maintenance issues. If leased, provide the lease terms.) A free online tool and manual for valuing the energy production of the Solar PV System is available at www.pvvalue.com Download the PV Value™ Manual for explanation of the solar terms on this form and inputs used in the PV Value Tool.	Discuss source of information and define other renewable energy sources, such as wind, hydropower, biomass power, etc. The property owner did not have the solar PV paperwork supplied by the installer. The details of the system were obtained from a phone interview with the installer. The only item not available was the exact tilt; therefore, the latitude is the default used by the PV Value software. No shading of the panels was visible and the system in being monitored. The homeowner present was not familiar with how to provide a monitoring report of the energy produced at this point; therefore, the energy production shown on the PV Value tool estimate is assumed to be reasonable. The installer indicated that the estimate is reasonable. The $5,000 in incentives is expected from the state to offset the cost of the system. The incentive has not been received as of the date of the appraisal but is expected soon by the property owner.

FEATURE	SUBJECT	COMPARABLE SALE # 1	+(-) $ Adjustment	COMPARABLE SALE # 2	+(-) $ Adjustment	COMPARABLE SALE # 3	+(-) $ Adjustment
Address	Electric Row Wishing	Fox Fire St. Wishing		Silver Lining St. Wishing		Boxer Ln. Wishing	
Proximity to Subject		0.25 mi. E		0.18 mi. S		0.45 mi. N	
Sale Price	$ 285,000	$ 260,000		$ 280,000		$ 265,000	
Sale Price/Gross Liv. Area	$ 118.75 sq. ft.	$ 118.75 sq. ft.		$ 107.69 sq. ft.		$ 108.16 sq. ft.	
Data Source(s)		MLS 45605		MLS 65301		MLS 435678	
Verification Source(s)		Agent		Agent		Agent	
VALUE ADJUSTMENTS	DESCRIPTION	DESCRIPTION	+(-) $ Adjustment	DESCRIPTION	+(-) $ Adjustment	DESCRIPTION	+(-) $ Adjustment
Sale or Financing		Cash		Conventional		Conventional	
Concessions		None		None		None	
Date of Sale/Time		2 months ago		4 months ago		6 months ago	
Location	Quiet Street	Quiet Street		Quiet Street		Quiet Street	
Leasehold/Fee Simple	Fee simple	Fee simple		Fee simple		Fee simple	
Site	14,000 Sq. Ft.	12,800 Sq. Ft.		13,490 Sq. Ft.		12,000 Sq. Ft.	
View	Residential	Residential		Residential		Residential	
Design (Style)	Salt Box-2 story	Salt Box-2 story		Salt Box-2 story		Cape Cod 1.5 St.	
Quality of Construction	Good	Good		Good		Good	
Actual Age	3 +/- Years	2 Years		1 Year		4 Years	
Condition	Good	Good		Good		Good	
Above Grade	Total / Bdrms. / Baths	Total / Bdrms. / Baths		Total / Bdrms. / Baths		Total / Bdrms. / Baths	
Room Count	8 / 4 / 3	8 / 4 / 2.5	2,000	8 / 4 / 3		7 / 3 / 2.5	2,000
Gross Living Area	2,400 sq. ft.	2,200 sq. ft.	9,000	2,600 sq. ft.	-9,000	2,450 sq. ft.	0
Basement & Finished	Full/1,200 Sq. Ft.	Full/1,100 Sq. Ft.		Full/1,300 Sq. Ft.		Full/1,100 Sq. Ft.	
Rooms Below Grade	90% Finished	100% Finished		95% Finished		100% Finished	
Functional Utility	Average	Average		Average		Average	
Heating/Cooling	FWA C/Air	FWA C/Air		FWA C/Air		FWA C/Air	
Energy Efficient Items	Net-Zero Energy	HERS 56	13,000	HERS 45	13,000	HERS 75	18,000
Garage/Carport	2-Car Garage	2-Car Garage		2-Car Garage		2-Car Garage	
Porch/Patio/Deck	Covered Entry	Covered Entry		Covered Entry		Covered Entry	
	1 F/P	1 F/P		1 F/P		1 F/P	
	45	35		75		55	
	$280,000	$275,000		$295,000		$270,000	
Net Adjustment (Total)		[x] + [ ] -	$ 24,000	[x] + [ ] -	$ 4,000	[x] + [ ] -	$ 20,000
Adjusted Sale Price of Comparables		Net Adj. 9.2 % / Gross Adj. 9.2 %	$ 284,000	Net Adj. 1.4 % / Gross Adj. 7.9 %	$ 284,000	Net Adj. 7.5% / Gross Adj. 7.5%	$ 285,000

Comparable Sale 2 has a lower HERS Index than the subject property had prior to the solar installation and is a comparable structure. However, it does not have solar PV panels, so a solar adjustment is applied.

Comparable Sale 3 is a code-built house with a higher HERS Index than the subject property had prior to the solar installation. Because the comparable property is not as energy efficient, it required a larger adjustment for energy efficiency. The basis for this energy-efficiency adjustment (not considering solar) is the comparison of this sale to Comparable Sale 1, the property of the most similar size. The comparison of paired sales supports a $5,000 adjustment for the energy-efficient structure plus $13,000 for the solar PV adjustment.

The contributory value of the solar PV system is based on the present value of the energy produced. The results of the application of the PV Value tool and support for the inputs are included in the appraisal report, and these conclusions support a rounded value range for the system of between $12,700 (rounded) and $14,550 (rounded). A reconciled adjustment of $13,000 is applied based on this range. The three-month-old solar PV system cost $27,500, and the owner received $5,000 in incentives for a net cost of $22,500, a figure slightly higher than what the market will support at this time. The contributory value of $13,000 derived from the PV Value software is also applied in the cost approach under the "as is value of site improvements" line item.

The gross and net adjustments are well within secondary mortgage market guidelines. The adjustment for energy efficiency is well supported, and the data supports a tight range after adjustments are applied for other minor differences. The subject property's sale price is within the adjusted price range, supporting the value at $285,000.

This example is simple, but it illustrates how the adjustment for energy-efficient items must be carefully analyzed when alternative energy is involved. Comparable Sale 3 in Exhibit 11.5 represents a code-built house without a solar PV system. It required an adjustment for the lower efficiency of the structure plus the lack of a solar PV system. However, that same adjustment would not apply to the first two comparable sales because they had energy-efficient structures identified by the HERS Index ratings that were similar to the subject property, but no solar PV systems.

Steps Toward More Efficient Transactions Involving High-Performance Housing

SITE WATER ENERGY AIR QUALITY MATERIALS MAINTENANCE

A number of problems associated with green housing have been discussed throughout this text, and solving these problems requires efforts from all segments of the real estate market. Builders, lenders, underwriters, participants in the secondary mortgage market, real estate agents, developers, property raters, and appraisers must continue to work together to further the progress made so far in reducing misunderstandings and inefficiencies in sales and lending transactions involving high-performance properties.

Appraisers can take a variety of steps to help their clients and the broader group of market participants understand and more effectively deal with the challenges associated with high-performance housing. This chapter outlines these steps and helps put the issues and challenges presented throughout this book into a larger perspective.

Step 1. Network with Other Professionals and Educate the Public

Real estate agents, builders, third-party raters, and appraisers can play important roles in educating the public on the attributes and economic advantages of high-performance houses. Until the public becomes knowledgeable about the benefits of green features, it will be difficult to convince buyers to pay a premium or seek out green homes over standard homes.

Local chapters of the National Association of Home Builders, the Appraisal Institute, the US Green Building Council, and the National Association of Realtors often seek speakers for their luncheon or dinner meetings. This presents a great opportunity for appraisers to network with other professionals and brainstorm ways different groups can work together to make transactions of high-performance homes go more smoothly.

Step 2. Qualify the Sales Agent

Owners of high-performance houses seeking real estate agents to list their homes for sale should qualify the agents' knowledge of this property type. In order to sell a house, an agent must have knowledge of its physical and economic characteristics. The best price can be gained when a good salesperson with knowledge of the product's selling points is involved.

More real estate agents should take courses in green building. To date, less than 2% of all licensed real estate agents in the United States have taken the green classes offered by the National Association of Realtors.

For example, a newly constructed, net-zero energy house was recently advertised in my local paper, and it sparked my interest. When I visited the sales office, I noticed that it had various displays of high-performance features, including a large reproduction of the HERS Index scale. When I asked the sales agent if I could take a photo of the HERS scale, he said, "Sure, but I have no clue what it means." Do you think this agent could convince a buyer that a green house should sell for more because it has a zero HERS Index rating?

Step 3. Prominently Advertise High-Performance Features

MLS listings and builders' promotional materials for new homes often fall short in the category of marketing and usually only focus on the gross living area and the number of bedrooms and bathrooms. Appraisers often review listings, newspaper advertisements, and promotional materials to find data, including sales, current list prices, costs of new homes, and predominantly advertised features. However, you can pick up any magazine or newspaper with new home listings and ads and see that very few advertisements provide any more information than the living area, parking options, number of bedrooms and bathrooms, and price. If high-performance features are valuable and sought by the market, shouldn't they be prominently listed in the advertisements? If sales materials don't promote any green features, why would a buyer, appraiser, or underwriter think that high-performance attributes would sell at a premium?

Step 4. Qualify the Lender

Lenders and their underwriting guidelines vary widely. Lenders who do not sell loans on the secondary market (to Fannie Mae, Freddie Mac, the VA, or FHA) often have less stringent underwriting guidelines. Credit unions and small community banks often keep their loans in house and are therefore more likely to accept unusual houses for mortgage loans.

Appraisers should ask real estate agents and builders who deal with a variety of lenders to recommend those who understand high-performance properties and are willing to hire competent appraisers to value them.

The Federal Reserve Bank of Atlanta invited the Appraisal Institute's president, Richard L. Borges II, MAI, SRA, to speak at a forum in 2013. The goal of the forum was to bring together bank supervisors and industry participants to examine and discuss the challenges confronting the financial services industry and to promote an open discussion on how economic trends, financial market activities, and the regulatory environment would affect the banking industry in the near future.

Mr. Borges' speech summarized these lending difficulties as follows:

> We need a strong education effort for regulators, underwriters, and credit risk managers about the appraisal process. Bank regulators are inadequately trained and underfunded. At one point there were several hundred appraisers in the bank regulatory system. Today, there are roughly five total, and one agency doesn't have any.

Mr. Borges summarized the problems that the market faces in not only the valuation of high-performance properties but of all property types. Choosing lenders carefully by investigating them as thoroughly as you would your stockbroker is a step in the right direction.

For their part, builders and real estate agents might consider using the following wording as part of a lending agreement once a qualified lender seems to have been found:

> This Home is being built/renovated/updated to nationally recognized standards above prevailing code. It is designed and constructed with unique features and materials and with high-efficiency equipment and in accordance with high-efficiency standards. The Lender shall choose an Appraiser educated and knowledgeable in this type of valuation of these specialized Homes, preferably an appraiser who holds a professional appraisal designation that requires advanced education on such issues as the valuation of sustainable buildings (e.g., MAI or SRA designations from the Appraisal Institute). The appraiser shall provide verification of green valuation education of 14 hours or more from a qualified educational provider and knowledge to be permitted to conduct the appraisal for this project.

As discussed in Chapter 3, the original version of this statement was written by Matt Belcher, the director of the High Performance Building Center at the Midwest Energy Efficiency Research Consortium, University of Missouri-Columbia. It was then modified by the National Association of Homebuilders to include a minimum number of hours of green valuation education and the participation of designated appraisers who have completed education in the valuation of sustainable buildings.

Step 5. Qualify the Appraiser

Appraisers should, of course, be qualified just as sales agents and lenders should be. Prior to hiring an appraiser or making an appointment with one, the nonappraiser should ask the following questions:

- Can you name the six elements of green building? (They are listed on the Appraisal Institute's Residential Green and Energy Efficiency Addendum.)

- Have you completed any green valuation education? How many hours of green valuation education have you completed? Can you provide proof of completion?
- Have you appraised a green house before?
- What documents do you need to have available at the time of the site visit?
- Will you be using the Appraisal Institute's Residential Green and Energy Efficient Addendum?

The answers to these questions will provide good insight into an appraiser's qualifications and competency. If the appraiser has not taken any green valuation courses, cannot name the six elements of green building, and indicates that no special documents are needed for the site visit, you may have the wrong person for the job. The next call should be to the lender to request a more qualified appraiser. This doesn't mean that the first appraiser is not competent in all property types, he or she has just not shown sufficient evidence of competency in valuing high-performance properties.

Step 6. Prepare and Distribute the Necessary Documents

Certain documents are essential for supporting the conclusions that appraisers need to communicate to their clients and sometimes educate their clients about. The following documents are some of the most important ones that appraisers should prepare and be prepared to distribute to their clients:

- HERS Index rating with estimated monthly or annual energy savings
- Home Energy Score (for existing homes)
- Green Rating score and worksheet that details points awarded
- Energy Star certificate (for Energy Star homes)
- Plans and specifications (for newer construction)
- Cost breakdown (for newer construction)
  (For example, identify green cost premiums with green ink)
- List of incentives for high-performance features that offset costs (for proposed construction)
- Comparison table of code-built versus high-performance structures with specification of the code used (as illustrated in Exhibit 12.1)

Step 7. Provide Comparable High-Performance Sales, Listings, or Listings Under Contract

The sales agent, builder, or homeowner should provide the appraiser with addresses of properties that sold within the last year and that are

Exhibit 12.1	Sample Comparison of a Code-Built versus a High-Performance Structure	
Feature	**Code-Built**	**High-Performance**
HERS Index	90	56
Estimated monthly utility	$145	$75
Wind load	150	165
Windows	Double pane	Low-E
HVAC/air	14 SEER/95% efficient	19 SEER/98% efficient
Incentives/rebates	$0	$2,500 for HVAC 19 SEER

similar to the property being appraised. Appraisers are required to verify sales prior to using them in their analyses. Lenders often require one listing and one pending listing in addition to closed sales. Appraisers are not obligated to use these sales provieded by the property owner, sales agent, or builder, but if they are qualified comparable sales that fall within the secondary mortgage market guidelines, they will most likely be used. According to most underwriting guidelines, the best comparable sales are those that have occurred within the last six months to one year, are located less than a mile from the subject property, and warrant adjustments that do not exceed a 25% gross adjustment or 15% net adjustment. Appraisers can use sales that are not specifically within these guidelines as additional comparable sales, but the relevance of these additional sales would require explanation.

In the next chapter, we'll sum up the history of green residential properties and the current state of high-performance housing and discuss where green housing is likely to be headed in the future.

Conclusion

SITE WATER ENERGY AIR QUALITY MATERIALS MAINTENANCE

It has long been a common practice to bring stakeholders together to develop a plan in the preliminary stages of any green project. These stakeholders have included builders, designers, owners, construction tradespeople, green raters, and energy modelers. However, some extremely important stakeholders—lenders, appraisers, and sales agents—have historically been omitted from the planning stage of green projects and thus lag behind in terms of knowledge of green building technology and its benefits. This may be a major cause of many of the green valuation, lending, and selling problems experienced today.

Of course, green construction has been a part of American history well before any green certifying organizations were formed. For hundreds of years, Native Americans in the Southwest region of the country built thick-walled adobe structures that took advantage of their orientation in relation to the sun. In the 1800s, Florida cracker architecture became popular in the state it was named after. Florida cracker houses were raised off the ground to avoid moisture, and these houses also made use of large overhangs, wraparound porches, high ceilings, large windows, and shallow building depths for cross-ventilation purposes. In the 1920s and 1930s, solar water heaters were used in Coral Gables, Florida, which is one of the nation's first planned communities.

Green building is not such a new concept when you consider the history of building in this country; the names we give to better building techniques and testing methods have simply changed. If we stopped using the term *green* and simply introduced these types of homes as "good-quality" or "high-performance," would there be such a resistance to this type of construction?

The market for high-performance homes is clearly growing. Throughout this book, I've argued that better communication and data sharing are necessary to help transactions involving high-performance homes happen more smoothly. Providing education for all parties involved is a great place to start. Classes that provide the opportunity for builders, third-party certifiers, agents, and lenders to learn about and discuss green residential building can be extremely beneficial in opening the lines of communication.

These stakeholders, who historically have been omitted from the planning stage of green projects, have significant contributions to make to the conversation.

- *Lenders* provide mortgages or construction funds for green projects, and they can provide perspective on the difficulties that lenders, borrowers, and appraisers often encounter.

- *Sales agents* are expected to sell green features that they may know nothing about. Green construction has outpaced green educational offerings for agents. If agents were more engaged in the process, they could bring valuable information about what the local market would readily accept in terms of price from the planning table. They can also provide information about trends in what buyers are looking for in a home.

- *Appraisers* are expected to place values on green projects that are comparable to the projects' costs. Appraisers were expected to be competent in green building even before sufficient educational opportunities were in place. If appraisers are included in the planning conversation, they can provide information about general market problems that may translate to a value or price less than cost. Appraisers can also provide information about general market problems in valuing these types of properties that they anticipate in the near future.

Educational programs on high-performance properties are currently available for appraisers and agents.[1] However, these courses and seminars are often not well attended for the following reasons:

- High-performance houses make up a relatively small portion of the market at this time.

- Lenders do not require appraisers to complete the educational programs that would properly qualify them for complex assignments involving high-performance properties.

- Real estate agents have not seen any demand for them to complete such educational programs.

- Appraisal fees for assignments involving high-performance houses are not sufficient to compensate appraisers for the additional education needed to become competent. Therefore, appraisers may refuse to accept the appraisal assignments until the fees are increased.

When builders, buyers, sellers, and lenders begin seeking real estate professionals who have green valuation education and experience, more green courses will fill up.

On a more positive note, most segments of the real estate industry are beginning to have a healthy dialogue about green building. The

---

1. See, for example, the educational offerings at www.appraisalinstitute.org/education/green/default.aspx.

industry partners who are networking with each other on a regular basis will move the industry forward. It is my hope that this book can further promote this open dialogue and sharing of information and encourage even more sectors of the market to get involved.